Synopses of the British Fauna (New Series)
Edited by Doris M. Kermack and R. S. K. Barnes
No. 4
Second Edition

HARVESTMEN

Keys and notes for the identification of the species

P. D. HILLYARD

*Department of Zoology, British Museum (Natural History),
Cromwell Road, London, SW7 5BD*

and

J. H. P. SANKEY

3, Glenrose, Old London Road, Mickleham, Dorking, Surrey, RH5 6BY

1989
Published for
The Linnean Society of London
and
The Estuarine and Brackish-water Sciences Association
by
E. J. Brill
Leiden · New York · Copenhagen · Cologne

Library of Congress Cataloging-in-Publication Data
Hillyard, P. D.
    Harvestmen: keys and notes for the identification of the species
/ P. D. Hillyard and J. H. P. Sankey.—2nd ed.
        p.   cm.—(Synopses of the British fauna; new series no. 4)
    Bibliography: p.
    Includes index.
    ISBN 90-04-09078-9 (pbk.)
    1. Opiliones—Great Britain—Identification. 2. Arachnida—Great
Britain—identification. I. Sankey, J. H. P. (John H. P.)
II. Title. III. Series.
QL255.S95 n.s., no. 4   1989
[QL458.5]
591.9'41 s—dc19
[595.4'3'0941]   88-36691
                                                            CIP

                        ISSN 0082–1101
                        ISBN 90 04 09078 9

            Printed in Great Britain at The Bath Press, Avon

Harvestmen

P. D. HILLYARD
Department of Zoology, British Museum (Natural History),
Cromwell Road, London, SW7 5BD
and
J. H. P. SANKEY
3, Glenrose, Old London Road, Mickleham, Dorking, Surrey, RH5 6BY

Contents

Foreword

Harvestmen is the second edition of *British Harvestmen* which was published in 1974 and *No. 4* in the *Synopses of the British Fauna (New Series)*. John Sankey was one of the authors in the first edition, and it is a pleasure to note that he is also an author in this second edition. A glance will show that this new edition is quite different from the first both in content and illustration. This is due to Paul Hillyard, who in addition to writing the text with John Sankey has drawn a completely new set of text-figures, which illustrate clearly the taxonomic features as well as the shape and characteristic posture of each species. Harvestmen are difficult animals to draw as when alive they seldom stay still and when dead they take on 'shrivelled' poses which are quite unlike those of the living animals. The Editors are grateful to him for the care he has taken to follow *Synopsis*-style and to John Sankey for his valuable help.

Below is a reprint of *A Historical Note*, which appeared in the first edition of *No. 4* in the *New Series* and it shows that John Sankey was one of its authors along with Mr. T. H. Savory, who produced the first and original *Synopsis* in 1943. Those that are acquainted with the latter will appreciate the wealth of information that has been acquired during the intervening years. The Editors hope that others besides the members of the British Arachnological Society will find this *Synopsis* invaluable in identifying British harvestmen and that they will send their specimens and locality data to the Biological Records Centre at Monks Wood Experimental Station, Abbots Ripton, Huntingdon, PE17 2LS, so that the *Provisional Atlas of the harvest-spiders*, compiled by John Sankey can be brought fully up to date.

R. S. K. Barnes   Doris M. Kermack
Estuarine and Brackish-water   The Linnean Society
Sciences Association   of London

A Historical Note

British Harvestmen – Synopsis of the British Fauna (New series) No. 4 can be regarded as a third edition and has a history dating back to 1942. In July of that year Mr. T. H. Savory gave an account of the biology of British Opiliones to the Crustacea Committee of the Linnean Society. This paper was obviously of wider interest and so was read to a general meeting of the Society on 23rd March 1943 (*Proc. Linn. Soc.* 155, 81–92). Then it was announced that the account would be published separately as the first of a series of ecological fauna lists to be sponsored by the Linnean Society's sectional committees, i.e. as the first *Synopsis of the*

British Fauna. The late Mr. D. M. Reid, secretary of the Crustacea committee, was the editor of the *Synopses* of which eight titles were produced from 1943 until 1949. These little handbooks were very popular and a number of them, including *No. 1 – Opiliones (Arachnida) or Harvestmen* (1948) appeared as second editions or reprints. During the period 1954–64, there were further reprintings and the range of titles extended until there were 14 in all. The *New Series* was started in 1970.

It is therefore a particular pleasure to introduce *British Harvestmen* as *No. 4* in the *New Series of Synopses* with Mr. T. H. Savory as one of the joint-authors with Mr. J. H. P. Sankey. This synopsis has been completely rewritten and contains many new illustrations. The Society is truly grateful to the authors for undertaking this work and also for the care they have taken to see that the format follows closely that of *British Ascidians, British Prosobranchs* and *British Marine Isopods*, which have already appeared as the *New Series Synopses*.

As in previous *New Series Synopses*, spaces have been left in the text for the owner's notes and records and the cover is water-proofed, so that this can be truly described as a working field and laboratory pocket book filling the gap between specialist monographs and popular field guides. It is hoped that it will meet the needs of the amateur naturalist, sixth-form pupils and undergraduates, whilst also being of value to professional zoologists.

DORIS M. KERMACK – Editorial Secretary, Linnean Society.

Introduction

The character of harvestmen was most amusingly described by Savory (1977): 'The harvestmen are surely the comedians among Arachnida: animals with rotund bodies ornamented with little spikes, with two eyes perched atop, back to back, like two faces of a clocktower, with ungainly legs insecurely attached, with feeble jaws and an undying thirst – a queer assortment of characters, even among a queer folk.' One might add that they are so inoffensive that even arachnophobic people may warm to them and express admiration for their remarkable legs. Indeed, the legs of many harvestmen are extremely long and thin and are controlled, rather amazingly, from a body which seems too small (Fig. 1).

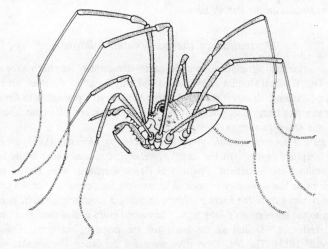

Fig. 1. *Rilaena triangularis* – a typical harvestman

Harvestmen: their identity

The harvestmen, or harvest-spiders, constitute the order Opiliones of the class Arachnida (subphylum Chelicerata). Their relatives within the Arachnida include the mites, spiders, scorpions and pseudoscorpions (see *Synopsis No. 40*). Arachnids and the rest of the chelicerates are distinguished from other arthropods by having a body which is divided into two parts: an anterior cephalothorax (prosoma) and a posterior abdomen (opisthosoma). They possess a pair of chelicerae, a pair of pedipalps and four pairs of legs but they have no antennae or mandibles and their eyes are simple, i.e. not compound as in insects and crustaceans.

Arachnids are essentially terrestrial and, with the exception of many mites, are mostly predatory, other arthropods forming the principal prey.

Probably because in both spiders and harvestmen the legs are usually long in relation to the size of the body, the two groups are often confused. The simplest distinction lies with the abdomen which in the case of spiders is unsegmented and narrowly joined to the cephalothorax. In harvestmen the abdomen does show evidence of segmentation and it is broadly joined to the cephalothorax giving the appearance of a one-piece body (Figs 2 & 3). Further distinctions from spiders may be found in Table 1.

Among the other British Arachnida only mites (subclass Acari) could possibly be confused with harvestmen (Table 1). However, mites are usually so much smaller than harvestmen (neglecting the large acarines known as ticks) that difficulty in separating them could only possibly arise with very young harvestmen. The exception to this is found among the Opiliocariformes (the 'mite-harvestmen'). This order comprises a single family of brightly coloured, omnivorous, primitive mites which resemble harvestmen. However, they occur only accidentally in the British Isles.

Derivation of the names and folklore

The connection with agriculture, as in the name 'harvestman', has been a recurrent theme. Dr. Thomas Mouffet (1634) explained why he knew them as 'shepherd spiders': 'The English call it shepherd either because it is pleased with the company of sheep or because shepherds think those fields that are full of them be good wholesome sheep pasture . . .'

The name *Phalangium opilio* given to a species by Linnaeus (1758) probably means 'shepherd spider'. In the Greek, *phalangion* means spider while in the Latin, *opilio* means shepherd. Possibly as Greek shepherds were known to use stilts the name has some significance. Alternatively the derivation for the generic name may come from the Latin *phalanga* meaning a long pole or staff, again an allusion to the harvestman's long legs. The name *Opilio* is also used as a generic name (Herbst, 1798) and as the basis for the name of the order Opiliones (Sundevall, 1833). The old, alternative name for the order, Phalangida, is now invalid (*Derivation of the scientific names*, p. 100).

In France, where there is a similar connection to harvest-time, the season of greatest abundance, harvestmen are known as 'les faucheurs' (reapers). In Germany they are called 'die Weberknechte' (weavers' servants). In North America and in this country they are popularly known as 'daddy-longlegs' but here the name is also applied to crane-flies (Diptera: Tipulidae). In 1746 B. Martin called them 'carter' or 'father-longlegs'; they were also known as 'Harry-longlegs'.

Bristowe (1949) comments that the ease with which harvestmen shed their legs must have contributed to the cruel custom at Llanidloes (Powys) of plucking the legs off one by one and throwing the poor remnant to the ground while reciting the following lines:

Old Harry long legs
Cannot say his prayers
Catch him by the right leg
Catch him by the left leg
And throw him downstairs

Status of harvestmen

Worldwide the total number of species of harvestmen is unknown; undoubtedly there are many still to be described. Possibly the total fauna at the present time is in the region of 3500–5000 species. This is approximately one tenth the size of the spiders (order Araneae). In British terms the total of 23 species of native harvestmen is about one twenty seventh the number of British spiders (c. 630). Our 23 species of harvestmen may be compared with the 21 known from Holland (Spoek, 1963) and the total of 110 found in Europe north of the Mediterranean (Martens, 1978).

Unfortunately harvestmen have not received a great deal of scientific attention. Detailed biological and behavioural information for many species is still lacking; for tropical species it is virtually non-existent. It cannot be claimed that harvestmen have much medical or commercial importance, but they are often a significant part of the invertebrate community and in some ecosystems, particularly in the tropics, the harvestmen may be present in such numbers that they constitute a greater predatory force than that of the spiders (Dalingwater, 1983).

4

Table 1 *Comparison of British harvestmen, spiders and mites*

	Harvestmen (Opiliones)	Spiders (Araneae)	Mites and ticks (Acari)
Body	One piece, abdomen and cephalothorax broadly joined	Two part, abdomen and cephalothorax joined by a narrow pedicel	One piece, abdomen and cephalothorax fused
Abdomen	Segmented	Unsegmented	Evidence of segmentation in some
Second pair of legs	Always longest	Longest only in some families	Not normally the longest
Chelicerae	Three articles	Two articles	Three articles but often modified
Eyes	Two	Eight, sometimes less	None to five
Odoriferous or stink glands	Present	Absent	Absent
Venom glands	Absent	Only rarely absent	Probably absent
Silk glands	Absent	Always present (in abdomen)	Present in some (in pedipalp)
Mating	Direct, by copulation. Little courtship	Indirect. Courtship often elaborate	Direct or indirect transference of sperm
Eggs	Laid in soil or other damp medium	Usually protected in silk cocoons	Varied
Metamorphosis	None or slight	None or slight	Six-legged larval stage
Feeding	Carnivorous and saprophytic, rarely phytophytic	Carnivorous, rarely saprophytic	Carnivorous, parasitic, saprophytic or phytophytic
Number of British species	23	About 630	Approximately 1500

General structure

Structure of body

A harvestmen's body is approximately oval or subrectangular in shape when viewed dorsally or laterally (Figs. 2A & 3A). As in all Arachnida the body comprises an anterior portion, the **prosoma** or **cephalothorax**, and a posterior portion,

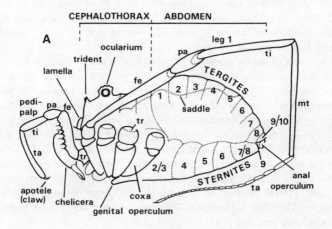

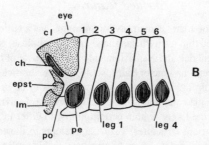

Fig. 2. A. Lateral view of body of typical harvestman; *tr* trochanter; *fe* femur; *pa* patella; *ti* tibia; *mt* metatarsus; *ta* tarsus. Fig. 2. B. Original (primitive) segmentation of cephalothorax in generalised, adult arachnid (after Snodgrass, 1948). The diagram shows the prosomatic, or pre-cheliceral, material (stippled) and six segments each of which bears a pair of appendages. Note that the prosomatic material is invaded by the primarily postoral chelicerae (*ch*); *cl* cephalic lobe; *epst* epistome; *lm* labrum; *po* pre-oral food cavity, *pe* pedipalp.

6

the **opisthosoma** or **abdomen**. In harvestmen the two portions are broadly joined from side to side and not, as in spiders, joined by a narrow waist.

The cephalothorax is composed of **prosomatic** or **pre-cheliceral** material (such as the eyes) and six segments, each of which bears a pair of appendages (Fig. 2B). The six pairs of appendages are (from the front): one pair of **chelicerae**, one pair of **pedipalps**, and four pairs of **legs**. The six segments are mostly fused but the last two may indicate their original segmentation; usually they form separate **sclerites** and are referred to as the **mesopeltidium** and **metapeltidium**. The first four segments comprise the **propeltidium** (Fig. 3A).

The abdomen is composed of ten segments, none of which bears appendages, and the segmentation is more or less discernible throughout. It may be indicated by as many as eight or nine dorsal sclerites, as in Phalangiidae, or by a single **dorsal shield** as in Trogulidae. Where distinct, the segments are usually marked by transverse grooves and, or, by rows of tubercles in the centre of each dorsal sclerite (*Surface features*, below).

The structure of the abdomen is more complicated than it appears. Each of the ten abdominal segments comprises a dorsal **tergite** and a ventral **sternite**. The tergites, numbered 1–10, correspond with the sternites, numbered 2–9, plus the **anal operculum**. However, it is a feature of the order Opiliones that the corresponding tergites and sternites are not dorso-ventrally opposite each other. Through studies of embryonic development, Winkler (1957) discovered that the first sternite is reduced but the first tergite is normally developed. Thus the gap left by the reduction of sternite 1 has been filled by the forward translocation of the other sternites. Consequently, the anal operculum has moved from a terminal to a more ventral position while some of the posterior tergites have bent downwards. The effect has been that Opiliones typically have shorter bodies than other Arachnida (see also p. 10).

Surface features

The surface covering of a harvestman, its **integument**, has a **cuticle** which varies from relatively soft and thin as in Phalangiidae and Leiobunidae, to more strongly **sclerotized** as in Trogulidae and Nemastomatidae. The cuticle of body, limbs and other appendages presents a range of **hairs**, **setae**, **spines**, **denticles** and **tubercles** which together make up the 'armature'. Armature tends to be more pronounced in males but generally the condition is notoriously variable. Individuals of a given species (intraspecific) are likely, within certain limits, to differ in the number and development of the various structures. Figure 5 attempts to illustrate and present a nomenclature for the different classes of armature visible on British harvestmen under an ordinary light microscope. This nomenclature is followed throughout.

Other structures visible on the surface of Opiliones such as **lyrifissures** (stress receptors, p. 20), microsculpture and the various forms of chemosensitive setae require high magnification and are not dealt with in great detail in this volume. The reader is referred to Barth & Stagl (1976), Martens (1978) and Van der Hammen (1985).

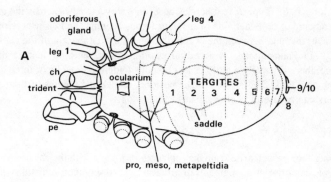

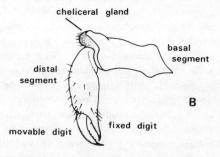

Fig. 3. A. Dorsal view of body of typical harvestman, *ch* chelicera; *pe* pedipalp. B. Lateral view, from inside, of right chelicera. Note: cheliceral gland found only in adult males in the families Nemastomatidae and Sabaconidae (p. 40 and 52).

Cephalothorax

The dorsal surface of the cephalothorax forms a relatively rigid **carapace**. In Nemastomatidae and Trogulidae the carapace forms a single shield with some or all of the abdominal tergites. Except in Trogulidae, the carapace carries, in a more or less central position, the **ocular tubercle** or **ocularium** which bears a pair of **simple eyes** directed sideways. Often the ocularium is furnished on top with two rows of dorsal tubercles, spicules or denticles (see Figs. 2A & 5). In Trogulidae the eyes are located at the base of semicircular projections which form a characteristic **hood** (Figs. 10C, 11C), or **cucullus**, covering the mouthparts.

The carapace also carries, in a lateral position, the openings of the **odoriferous** or **repugnatorial glands** Fig. 3A). Usually these are situated where the carapace overhangs the bases of the first and second pairs of legs. They are normally visible in dorsal or lateral view and are conspicuous in some species (p. 17).

The carapace may be variously adorned with tubercular outgrowths of the cuticle

8

('**armature**' p. 6). Typically, tubercles occur in transverse rows across the meso- and metapeltidia; on either side of the odoriferous openings and elsewhere on the lateral margins; and between the occularium and the front margin of the carapace (Fig. 5). In Phalangiidae, in a central position on the anterior margin of the carapace, there is usually a more or less obvious **trident** consisting of three close-set tubercles (Figs. 2A, 3A & 5). The position, angles and lengths of the trident members can be useful characters in identification.

Appendages

The appendages which arise from the cephalothorax begin with the chelicerae. The chelicerae comprise three segments or articles: a **basal segment**, a **distal segment** and a movable digit or **apotele**. The movable digit works against the fixed digit of the distal segment to form a grasping and cutting tool. The basal and distal segments are usually armed with various tubercles, denticles and setae, especially in the dorsal regions. In a number of species the form of the chelicerae is sexually dimorphic. In the male the chelicerae may be considerably enlarged and may present prominent **apophyses** on the basal and or distal segments (e.g. *Phalangium opilio*, p. 78, Fig. 23A). A **cheliceral gland** (Fig. 3B) is present in males of the families Nemastomatidae and Sabaconidae. Behind and to the side of the chelicerae lie the pedipalps; they resemble short walking legs. The pedipalps, or palps, are composed of six segments: (from the base) **coxa, trochanter, femur, patella, tibia** and **tarsus** (Fig. 2A). Their function is predominantly sensory but the **maxillary lobe** or **gnathobase** of the coxa (Fig. 4B) is associated with food assimilation and ingestion. All pedipalp segments possess some form of armature including spines, tubercles, denticles and setae. Trochanter and femur may present prominent spine-tipped tubercles, particularly on the ventral surface. In the males of Phalangiidae and Leiobunidae the tarsus may be provided with a longitudinal series of micro-denticles on the inner-lower surface (Fig. 5E).

The relative lengths of the palpal tibia and tarsus are important in classification and so is the presence or absence of the tarsal claw together with its structure:

(a) claw absent – Nemastomatidae (p. 40–45), Sabaconidae (p. 52–54) and Trogulidae (p. 46–51);
(b) claw present, smooth – Phalangiidae (p. 58–59);
(c) claw present, pectinate or toothed – Leiobunidae (p. 90–99) and Sclerosomatidae (p. 55–57).

The four pairs of walking legs are each composed of seven segments, named as in the pedipalps but additionally with a metatarsus between tibia and tarsus. In all families the first pair of legs has a maxillary lobe on the coxa (Fig. 4B). In Phalangiidae, Leiobunidae and Sclerosomatidae the second (Fig. 4B) and sometimes the third coxae have maxillary lobes.

Coxae and trochanters usually possess hairs and often tubercles. Femora, patellae and tibiae always have armature of some form including hairs, spines and rows of acute tubercles, denticles or spicules (Fig. 5). These three segments may be cylindrical in cross-section but, especially in Phalangiidae, the cross-section may be angular, usually a pentagon.

The metatarsi may have a number of rings of false divisions which do not articulate. Where these divisions are present, the metatarsus (Fig. 2A) is divided into a basal **astragalus** (without false divisions) and a distal **calcaneus** (with false divisions). The tarsi normally have many articulating subdivisions giving them great flexibility. The tarsi of leiobunids may have as many as 100 or more segments but in Trogulidae the tarsus is never divided into more than four segments.

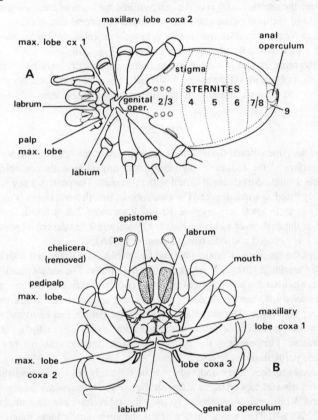

Fig. 4. A. Ventral view of body of typical harvestman, *max.* maxillary; *cx* coxa; *oper.* operculum. B. Antero-ventral view of mouthparts and surrounding structure of typical harvestman (see 'myliosoma', page 10), *pe* pedipalp, *max.* maxillary.

Mouthparts and sternum

The mouthparts of an opilionid are characterised by 1) their ventral position; 2) a curved pharynx and 3) the involvement of the *coxapophyses* of the palp and

9

anterior legs during food ingestion. This condition is known as **coxisternal feeding** and also occurs in scorpions, horseshoe crabs and fossil eurypterids. In opilionids solid material is ingested and then digested internally.

The elements comprising the mouthparts (Fig. 4B) are: chelicerae, **labrum** and **epistome** (clypeus), pedipalps, mouth, pharynx, **labium** and the coxapophyses of the palps and anterior legs. Together with the cheliceral frame (cheliceral attachment region) and the **myliosomatic apodeme**, the entire structure involved in coxisternal feeding is termed the **myliosoma** by Van der Hammen (1985).

Between the anterior margin of the carapace and the bases of the chelicerae there lies a fold of laminate tissue known as the **supra-cheliceral lamella** (Fig. 2A). In the family Nemastomatidae the lamella is heavily indented; in *Phalangium opilio* it bears a pair of small but prominent tubercles (Fig. 23B).

The **sternum**, normally visible in arachnids, can usually only be revealed by dissection. In Opiliones (Palpatores) it is largely obscured by the genital operculum in its forward position and also by the coxapophyses of the legs.

Abdomen

As previously mentioned, the abdomen is composed of ten original segments. The dorsal surface of the abdomen may present as many as nine discrete sclerites or constitute a single dorsal shield (fused with prosoma). The posterior segments are invariably fused to some degree. The condition in British harvestmen (Palpatores) typically is as follows: tergites 9 & 10 fused; sternites 7 & 8 fused; sternite 10 represents the anal cover and is surrounded by sternite 9. As described previously, sternite 1 is reduced and effectively absent (Fig. 2A).

Most of the species in Phalangiidae and Leiobunidae are decorated with a dorsal pattern of markings (Figs. 2A, 3A) known as the **saddle**. The saddle usually forms a dark central band which may cover the anterior two thirds or the entire length of the abdomen. Often the saddle appears to be a continuation of dark markings on the cephalothorax. The shape and details of the pattern can be useful in identification but considerable intraspecific variation exists especially in levels of pigmentation. Furthermore, the pattern may lack contrast with the rest of the abdomen, particularly in females.

The dorsal surface of the abdomen may be relatively smooth or furnished with transverse rows of tubercles. In a few species, e.g. *Homalenotus quadridentatus* p. 56 and *Mitostoma chrysomelas* (p. 44). the tubercles have an unusual form (Figs. 5, 10, 14). The ventral surface of the abdomen usually lacks tuberculations but may be quite hirsute as in *Sabacon* (Fig. 13A).

The **genital operculum** (Figs. 4A, B), a fold of tissue which covers the reproductive organs when at rest, occupies a forward position between the leg coxae but is largely derived from the second abdominal sternite and part of the third sternite, the first sternite being reduced. Through evolution the genital operculum probably has come to occupy an advanced position on the ventrum because of the particular method of copulation in Opiliones (except Cyphophthalmi) (Fig. 6 and p. 13). The **genital opening**, through which pass the extrusible reproductive

11

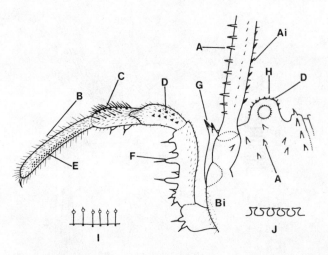

Fig. 5. Terminology of tuberculate structures (also see text). A. Acute, black-tipped tubercle; Ai. Acute, inclined tubercle; B. Seta; Bi. Hairs; C. Spine. D. Denticle. E. Micro-denticle. F. Spine-tipped tubercle. G. Trident. H. Spicule. I. 'Capitate' setae as found on pedipalps of Nemastomatidae. J. Series of bifid tubercles as found on the dorsum of *Mitostoma chrysomelas*.

organs, may be found under the leading edge of the genital operculum in adults. In immature specimens the operculum remains sealed.

On sternite 3, to the rear of the genital operculum, lie the **respiratory stigmata**. These two apertures are each situated close to the posterior edge of coxa 4 and may, in fact, be hidden by a fold in the integument (p. 20).

Reproductive organs

The sex organs (**penis** and **ovipositor**) lie behind the genital operculum when at rest. They originate as prolongations of the internal reproductive system (Fig. 6). The ovipositor is a broad mobile tube made up of approximately 20–40 membranous rings. It is usually bilobed terminally and furnished with groups of setae. Taxonomically, the characters of the ovipositor are useful only at family level and above.

The penis is a more rigid structure than the ovipositor. In Palpatores (all British harvestmen) it comprises a trunk or **corpus**, a distal **glans** and a terminal **stylus** (Fig. 6C). The base of the corpus is usually enlarged to accommodate a muscle bundle. In Phalangiidae the glans at rest is usually held at an angle with the corpus. It is articulated, at the jointed zone, by a long tendon operated from the muscle. In *Paroligolophus agrestis* (p. 66, Fig. 17E) the corpus is extremely slender while the base is considerably enlarged. In *Leiobunum* (p. 90) the corpus is relatively short and has lateral keels (Figs. 30C, D). In *Mitopus* (p. 74) the reader should note the retractable bladder and the apophysis on the ventral surface of the glans (Figs. 21D, E). See *Identification* (p. 34) and *Preservation and Examination* (p. 29).

12

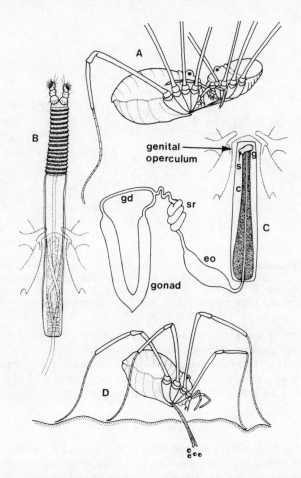

Fig. 6. Aspects of reproduction in typical harvestmen. A. Copulation: female left, male right – with penis extruded to enter genital operculum of female; B. Female ovipositor extruded through genital operculum; C. Male reproductive organs with penis retracted (adapted from Juberthie, 1964), *gd* gonoduct; *sr* seminal reservoir; *eo* expulsion organ; *c* corpus penis; *g* glans penis; *s* stylus; D. Female ovipositing eggs in substrate.

Biology

Life history, reproduction and moulting

Most British harvestmen have an annual life cycle. The typical species, i.e. the majority in the families Phalangiidae and Leiobunidae, hatch from the egg stage in the spring; they pass through several body stages (**instars**) during the spring and summer; and they become sexually mature later in the summer and autumn at which time the eggs are usually laid. Most individuals have died by the late autumn. Thus the typical harvestman lives for about six to seven months while the egg stage lasts for about five to six months.

A different seasonal pattern occurs in *Rilaena triangularis* (p. 86) and *Megabunus diadema* (p. 84): the eggs are deposited early (June and July) and they hatch in late summer; the young grow to near-adults and then over-winter in this condition, finally maturing during the following spring and early summer. To a degree, at least in favourable southern localities, *Phalangium opilio* (p. 78) combines the two patterns: both eggs and young may over-winter and two generations may occur in one year (Spoek, 1963); the population includes individuals in several stages of development at any one time.

A life cycle which takes more than twelve months is found in the families Trogulidae, Nemastomatidae and Sclerosomatidae. Here there is usually an overlap of generations as adults, young and eggs may all be present at any one time of the year. The egg-laying season is much less determinate than in other harvestmen and eggs from one batch may hatch soon after laying or, for example, a batch may have an extended period of hatching. *Mitostoma chrysomelas* (p. 44) is unusual (Meijer, 1984) in that individuals are short lived and reproduction may occur at any season.

By the standards of the Arachnida, mating in Opiliones is unusual in that it involves the use of a direct, intromittent male organ, i.e. the sexes perform copulation. It is also unusual in that it appears to be a casual affair with copulation occurring freely and frequently. However, the subject of their mating behaviour has received little attention and in a rare study by Edgar (1971) of North American *Leiobunum* species behaviour of some complexity was revealed. The author describes the formation of sexually mature groups, their positioning and timing; the periods of inactivity; the first encounters between the sexes; the occasional resistence of females and the conflicts among males.

Once begun, copulation is often repeated many times. Edgar records a male *Leiobunum longipes*, in the laboratory, which copulated at least 29 times over a period of two and a half hours. The act of copulation in Opiliones (Fig. 6A) is generally rather simple. The partners face each other while the male grasps the female with his pedipalps and extends his second pair of legs outwards to detect any interference. The penis is extruded through the male's genital operculum and the female may use her pedipalps and chelicerae to guide it to the oviduct through her genital opening. The duration of copulation can vary from a few seconds to several minutes depending on the species and the behaviour of the female. After mating both partners may mate again, either with each other or with different individuals.

Parthenogenesis, or asexual reproduction, can occur in some species. Phillipson (1959) found that a collection of 407 specimens of *Megabunus diadema* (p. 84) contained only one male (in all collections males are rare). To confirm the probability of parthenogenesis, Phillipson collected ten sub-adult females, with their genital operculum still sealed (thus unfertilized), and kept them in a laboratory in the absence of males. Over a period of some weeks seven of the females produced 13 batches of eggs all of which were found to be viable.

In nature, eggs are usually quite difficult to find. They are laid in batches in places such as damp soil, moist vegetable debris, the crevices of bark and under stones or dead wood. Eggs are usually spherical, creamy white, pale green or yellow but the eggs of trogulids are oval and are often laid in empty snail shells (Pabst, 1953). Eggs vary in size from about 0.5 mm diameter in *Nemastoma bimaculatum* (p. 42) to about 1.0 mm in *Odiellus spinosus* (p. 72). The number of eggs laid varies from an average of 73 per season in *N. bimaculatum* (1st year) and 30 (2nd year) to an average of 324, in four batches, in *Rilaena triangularis* (p. 86) (Phillipson, 1959). In the ten British species examined by Phillipson, the number of eggs laid was always only a fraction (21–57%) of the mean maximum number of eggs produced by the ovaries. The reason for this apparent wastage is not known.

Prior to hatching, the features of the young harvestman can be seen through the egg membrane. The eyes become conspicuous as a pair of dark patches at one pole and, approaching **eclosion**, the segmentation of the abdomen and the tightly curled limbs also become discernible. The initial rupture of the egg membrane is done by special 'egg tooth'. The nymphs undergo their first moult or **ecdysis** often within an hour of hatching. In some cases the first moulted exoskeleton may remain inside the egg-shell. The nymphs are feeble, ungainly creatures with uncertain control of their legs. The tarsi have fewer articulations than in the adult state. A recently hatched *Paroligolophus agrestis* (p. 66) has 8, 18, 8, 8 tarsal segments compared with 26 to 50 in the adult (Savory, 1977).

Development to the adult stage involves up to eight further moults. The number of moults and the intervals between depends to some extent on the rate of growth (Savory, 1977). The normal interval between moults is around ten days but the period may vary from six to twenty days. In nature, during periods of drought, it is usual for moulting activity to be much reduced. When the first rains do come, nearly all individuals in a population will have moulted within 24 hours (Edgar, 1971). In the laboratory, harvestmen often have difficulty with their ecdysis if temperature and humidity are not suitable (see p. 32).

When moulting, harvestmen (except Trogulidae) usually hang upside down in order to take advantage of gravity in withdrawing the long legs. Favoured places include the underside of leaves and branches, walls and tree trunks, and leaves in the litter. Sharp movements of the body and legs cause the exoskeleton to split. The chelicerae and the leg femora spring out at once through the tear followed by the rest of the body. Freeing the distal parts of the long legs is the difficult part of the process. The pedipalps grasp the bunch of legs, still partially encased in the old exoskeleton, and bring them towards the chelicerae. The legs are then individually pulled free by the chelicerae, each leg bent into a circle until the terminal claw is clear. When the legs are entirely free they are not immediately extended but are first threaded through the mouthparts to be cleaned. Finally the legs hang partially extended while the new chitin hardens. At each moult the legs increase their length considerably, up to as much as 150% of the previous length.

Legs and locomotion

The long or very long legs of harvestmen have probably evolved to meet the needs of prey-capture and defence in the particular types of habitat that they occupy. By virtue of their legs, harvestmen can traverse terrain such as long grass where other creatures, e.g. spiders and ants, are obliged to travel much more slowly.

Of the four pairs of legs the first, third and fourth pairs are essentially used for walking while the second pair, always the longest, is much more sensory in function. When the animal is on the move the second pair constantly tests the ground ahead; water, for example, is always touched by a second leg before advancing to drink. A harvestman which has lost one of its second pair of legs does not seem to be seriously handicapped but its behaviour is very different if both legs are lost; there are no rapid movements, no hastening to eat, drink or mate.

It is remarkable that limbs so vital to the animal's well-being should be lost so easily. A leg may be **autotomised** when escaping from a predator and will continue to jerk at the tibial-metatarsal joint. When picking-up a live harvestman it is difficult to avoid causing the loss of some limbs. A leg may even be lost trying to overcome surface tension when the animal extricates it from a drinking trough.

Harvestmen clean their legs meticulously in a process known as 'leg threading'. Each leg is held in the chelicerae and passed through the fleshy lobes of the mouthparts until the end of the tarsus is reached at which point it is bent almost into a circle. Finally it shoots out like a spring when released. Leg threading may occur even in the midst of other activities such as mating or running.

Harvestmen spend long periods with their legs stretched out from the body when resting, for example, on a wall or on the underside of leaves. The inactivity conserves water and energy and also gives protection from predators by the lack of movement. When harvestmen such as leiobunids are startled they may not immediately run but may bob up and down while the legs stay in place. Presumably this pumping up and down raises the temperature of the locomotory muscles and possibly helps move fresh air into the **tracheae**; after a short time the animal may stride away rapidly.

The evolution of long legs could not have come about without the necessary stability in the coxae (Manton, 1973). The coxae of most Opiliones are fixed and they fan out horizontally to reduce interference with each other. The legs themselves are of differential length so that their fields of movement overlap as little as possible. Opiliones, and indeed most arachnids, hang down from their legs unless they are very short. The patellae are directed upwards and the legs articulate principally at the trochanter-femur joint. There are many tarsal segments with a similar diameter; their combined effect facilitates climbing on vertical surfaces.

The thrust in the stepping movements is developed entirely in the segments beyond the trochanter. There is no evidence that the backstroke is produced by forces other than those generated by **intrinsic** and **extrinsic** muscles. Normal hydrostatic pressures in the **haemocoel** appear to be sufficient to cause leg extension when the tip is off the ground or exerting little force. The kind of dramatic increase in hydrostatic pressure within the body which produces, for example, the concerted jumping action of legs 3 and 4 in jumping spiders is unlikely to occur in opilionids (Manton, 1973).

Feeding

The available evidence suggests that most harvestmen are generalist feeders; the majority of small, soft-bodied arthropods and other invertebrates are likely to form suitable prey. The diet (as recorded by Bristowe, 1949 and Sankey, 1949b) includes: other harvestmen, small snails (chief food of trogulids), small earthworms, millipedes, spiders, earwigs, flies, mites, Collembola, aphids and leaf-hoppers. Edgar (1971) found that they feed ravenously on mayflies, caddis flies and dipterans. Sunderland and Sutton (1980) showed that most species of harvestmen are predators of woodlice, both immatures and adults, alive or dead.

Probably the majority of their food is caught alive and killed but a much wider range of foods than those mentioned above may be consumed when scavenging. Creatures such as centipedes, ants and beetles may be eaten if found dead and if the tough exo-skeleton is fractured. The extent to which harvestmen eat vegetable matter is questionable but a number of observers have recorded the chewing of fungi and soft fruits. Bristowe's observation (1949) that bird droppings constitute a food item is corroborated by one of us (JS).

Phillipson (1960a) gave a detailed account of feeding biology in *Mitopus morio* (p. 74). This study found that plant material is not eaten, at least in this species. Furthermore, *M. morio* eats only animals alive or recently dead and of a certain size and texture. Wingless forms were taken more quickly than winged. Phillipson found that a food capture was made only after contact with a leg had occurred. Because of a very poor sense of smell a trail of meat, for example, could not be followed. Feeding occurred at any time of day or night but there was an increased food intake during the hours of darkness, as is generally believed. The role of *M. morio* in general soil biology was discussed and expressed in figures of energy transfer. A difference in the metabolic rate of males and females was discovered. In a separate paper, Phillipson (1960b) detailed the food consumption of different instars of *M. morio* under natural conditions.

A young *Mitopus morio*, evidently hungry when captured, ate the whole of a clubionid spider at one sitting with a resultant swelling like that of a spider in similar circumstances (Savory, 1938). A male *Rilaena triangularis* (p. 86) spent four hours consuming a dead spider (*Pardosa lugubris*) leaving nothing but the exoskeleton and then devoured a second spider four hours later (*Ecology*, p. 27).

Water

Harvestmen in all stages need surroundings moist enough to prevent their desiccation; in such conditions they drink but little. Under dry conditions they soon become torpid and the leg tarsi may begin to curl. However, a harvestman apparently at the point of death will often make a complete recovery when given a drink. Drinking takes anything up to five minutes depending on thirst and the availability of water. The muscular pharynx produces a strong pumping action which can take up water quite rapidly. A capillary film of water is sufficient (Edgar, 1971).

Harvestmen will visit fallen or over-ripe fruit to suck the juices. In California, Harlow (1924) described the visit of harvestmen on several successive evenings to the inkwell on his desk; they readily drank red ink but refused black. In old age harvestmen are liable to drown themselves when they go to drink. This is not uncommon in captivity and it may well also occur in nature.

Enemies and defence

Edgar (1971) considered that spiders were probably the most important group of predators on harvestmen. Bristowe (1941), however, found that few spiders will sustain an attack on adult harvestmen apparently because of distastefulness. Probably some spiders will and some will not take harvestmen; their degree of hunger may also play a part.

Other harvestmen and other invertebrates such as centipedes and ground beetles will also feed on harvestmen. Bristowe (1949) included fish, frogs, toads and shrews as predators. Sankey (1949b) reported cases of harvestmen being eaten by badger, fox and hedgehog. British bird stomachs have been found to contain harvestmen but the most extensive data come from the USA where a survey of 80,000 bird stomachs yielded 9966 spiders, 795 harvestmen and 189 pseudoscorpions (Cottam, 1949).

Small, red, parasitic larval mites (Erythraeidae), e.g. *Leptus phalangii*, are frequently to be seen on the legs and body of harvestmen, as many as twenty at a time (Welbourn, 1983). Heavy infestations occur especially where the vegetation is luxuriant and the soil damp. Parasitic Hymenoptera, important enemies of spiders, have not as yet been recorded in association with harvestmen or their eggs (M. R. Shaw, pers. comm.). Microbial diseases of Arachnida, in particular fungal, rickettsial and viral infections were reviewed by Morel (1978).

Edgar (1971) recorded observations of frogs which were seen to rapidly expel harvestmen from their mouths. Undoubtedly this was because of the defensive fluid secreted by the odoriferous or repugnatorial glands (Fig. 3A). The chemistry of these **exocrine** secretions has been studied by Ekpa *et al*. (1985). In Palpatores they involve short-chained acylic ketones, alcohols and naphthoquinones. The chemical components have been found to have species-specific characteristics which are claimed to be of phylogenetic value.

In some species the fluid is expelled from the openings on the dorso-lateral surface of the cephalothorax as a fine spray, in others more slowly as a drop gradually increasing in size (Lawrence, 1938). An irritated *Leiobunum* will anoint its dorsal surface and pass some of the liquid to the ventral surface via processes on the coxae. A harvestman in such a condition is avoided by ants; should one grasp one of the harvestman's legs the limb will be rubbed against the body causing the ant to drop off and clean itself. Among British species the odour does not seem to be very noticeable to the human nose. However, Simon (1879) likened it to walnuts, Bristowe (1949) a 'strong and rather sweet odour' and Stipperger (1928) found it offensive, lasting for two minutes.

Defence takes other forms also. Long-legged species of harvestmen have the ability to put a safe distance between themselves and small predators particularly in habitats such as deep grass and foliage. A harvestman attacked above the ground or on a vertical surface will often defend itself by dropping down. When a leg is seized by a predator, or by the fingers of a collector, it parts readily at the femur-trochanter joint (autotomy) and remains twitching while its former owner escapes. Camouflage in harvestmen is best instanced by *Megabunus diadema* (p. 84) whose appearance blends well with the lichen which is invariably present in its habitat. The habit of catalepsy, or shamming death, certainly adds to the difficulty of seeing trogulids. A rigid trogulid may be picked up and turned over; with its legs pointing upwards it can maintain this position for some time.

Behavioural responses – 'Taxes'

Negative phototaxis, or movement away from light, is a standard behaviour in Opiliones. The young in particular show a strong tendency to shun light and hide in dark places but this trait reduces in later instars of those species which make vertical migrations.

Thigmotaxis, or the tendency to press the body against the substratum is a strongly marked characteristic. Captive animals frequently come to rest at the edges or corners of a container. In the wild it is common to find harvestmen pressed well into the crevices of rough bark, or hidden under a window ledge.

Harvestmen are positively **hydrotactic**, or sensitive to the presence of water, if the atmosphere is too dry or if they are thirsty. Probably it is this that brings them into our bathrooms, kitchens and damp outbuildings. A gravid female is able to detect soft damp ground suitable for laying eggs and for the survival of the frail young.

Rheotaxis, or the response to the movement of images across the retina, can be demonstrated in harvestmen. A movement outside a cage of *Leiobunum* (p. 90) will make the quiescent animals active; they may run round and round, their bodies rising and falling as they go until they all settle down again. As with Savory (1938) we have found that *Leiobunum* and *Dicranopalpus* (p. 92) may rise up and down on their long legs in a rather comical fashion if one's hand is moved up and down close by.

In a dense group of harvestmen an alarm stimulus may be transmitted rapidly through the many leg contacts. A large crowd was described in Wood's 'Natural History' of 1863: '. . . a legion of harvest-spiders, all gathered together, their little bodies nearly hidden by their long legs. There must have been thousands of creatures under the beam, all perfectly motionless'. Unfortunately such great densities seem no longer to be seen in Great Britain but J. Cloudsley-Thompson (pers. comm.) reports a large number of *Cosmobunus granarius*, perhaps 400, in a well at Moinho da Rocha (Portugal) in July 1985. Martens (1978) quotes the occurrence in Mexico of an association of about 700,000 individuals of *Leiobunum cactorum*.

Stridulation

This means of communication appears to be uncommon in harvestmen and has yet to be demonstrated in any species which occur in Britain. However, stridulation is known among several diverse groups of the order in South Africa, America, Europe and Turkey. Stridulatory organs usually present a series of parallel ridges which oppose another, similar series or some other form of scraper. Where stridulatory organs do occur (Martens, 1978) they may be variously located on:

1. The inner surface of the basal segment of the chelicera.
2. The inner surface of the second segment of the chelicera.
3. The inner surface of the femur of the pedipalp; stridulatory organs on the pedipalp may oppose either the outer surface of the chelicera or even the denticles on the ocularium.

Exoskeleton

In common with all Arthropoda, harvestmen have the need of an exoskeleton, as a barrier against the loss of internal fluids, for protection against injury, and as a support for the muscles. In cross-section the exoskeleton, or integument, is composed of up to six layers comprising:

(1) the basement membrane
(2) the hypodermal cellular layer
(3) the endocuticle
(4) the exocuticle
(5) the epicuticle
(6) the waxy layer

The exoskeleton is also the substrate for sense organs such as the eyes, spines, setae and lyriform organs. The tubercles which occur on the exoskeleton of harvestmen are hollow outgrowths of the cuticle, they are not sense organs. Similar outgrowths, but solid throughout, are known as denticles and when minute may be distinguished as spicules (p. 6 & Fig. 5). Spines are solid bristles, usually dark in colour. They may arise directly from the cuticle or from the end of a hollow tubercle. Spines are often arranged in rows and each communicates with a nerve ending. Setae are finer than spines, they tend to be erect and usually do not occur in rows. Hairs tend to be curved and shorter than setae. In Nemastomatidae the dense setae on the pedipalp are characteristically 'capitate' (Fig. 5I).

Lyriform organs, as in other Arachnida, are abundant on the exoskeleton of the body, pedipalps and legs, especially near the joints. Under the microscope, lyriform organs appear as slits in the cuticle; they may occur singly or in groups of parallel slits. On each of the legs, two groups lie either side of the trochanter-femur joint which is the plane of autotomy, the place of fracture when a leg is shed. Lyriform organs are mechanoreceptors (Barth & Stagl, 1976), with neural connections, which undergo minute deformations of the membrane in response to: airborne sounds, movements of parts of the body, the motion of walking and vibrations through the substrate. The legs of a harvestman radiate from the body and relay information about its surroundings in a way similar to that of the spider's web which passes vibrations to the spider at its centre.

Eyes

The eyes of opilionids are generally placed on the sides of an ocularium (except Trogulidae). The prominence of the ocularium was found by Juberthie (1964) to show a correlation between its height and the animal's habitat. Those species, e.g. *Nemastoma bimaculatum* (p. 42), which inhabit the darker recesses of litter etc. exhibit a regression of the visual apparatus. The opilionid eye is a typical ocellus with a single lens formed by a thickening of the cuticle (Curtis, 1970). The glassy body beneath the lens is made up of **lentigen cells** which vary in height in the different species according to their principal habitat, from as short as $2.5-3.0\,\mu$m in *N. bimaculatum* to $17.0\,\mu$m in *Opilio parietinus* (p. 80) and *Mitopus morio* (p. 74). A retina of visual cells bounded by pre- and post-retinal membranes makes up the back of the eye. The sense of sight is much less well developed than that of touch; probably the eyes do little more than register light intensities. There appears to be no evidence that the visual apparatus can form images.

Respiration

Opiliones respire by means of tracheae along which gaseous exchange, direct to the tissues, takes place. The tracheal structure resembles that of a branching, tubular network which opens to the exterior via a pair of stigma. The stigma lie within the third abdominal sternite and often occur in a depression alongside the fourth coxae (Fig. 4A). Additional apertures (**spiracles**) may occur also on the legs, particularly in the distal region of the tibiae. Tracheae here supply oxygen to the distal segments of the long legs. An autotomised leg, supplied with oxygen, can continue twitching for some time (Wasgestian-Schaller, 1967).

The spiracles and stigma are normally kept closed by muscles which relax only when the carbon dioxide content of the blood reaches or exceeds about 5% (Cloudsley-Thompson, 1988). In this way the loss of water, which inevitably accompanies respiratory exchange, is kept to a minimum. Like the integument of the body, the tracheae consist of cuticle (which is cast off at ecdysis) underlain by epidermal cells.

Phillipson (1960b) measured the rate of oxygen consumption in *Mitopus morio* (p. 74) and *Oligolophus tridens* (p. 62). The results give a comparison of their activities by day and by night over a period of 48 hours. The following figures refer to cubic millimetres of oxygen consumed per milligram of live weight per hour:

	First day	First night	Second day	Second night
M. morio	0.626	0.796	0.654	0.814
O. tridens	0.943	1.373	0.886	1.301

Homeostasis

In the laboratory, Todd (1949) tested the humidity and temperature preferences and limits of some common species of harvestmen. A strong correlation was observed between the laboratory results and the natural ecology of the species in oak woodland, i.e. their stratification and periods of activity. The figures were determined by noting the conditions in which the species tested were at equilibrium, i.e. came to rest. For five species the author gave also the heat death-point, a figure based on survivals counted ten hours after one hour's exposure to a high temperature in a saturated atmosphere. *Odiellus spinosus* (p. 72), for example, was found to have an exceptionally high heat death-point (c. 45.0°C) which is consistent with its southerly distribution in nature.

The following figures give some of the author's results:

Table 2

Field Data	Laboratory Data		
Preferred horizon and relative humidity (%) *Species*	*% humidity preference*	*Mean temp. preference*	*Heat death*
Branches 50–60 *O. hanseni*	46.8–54.8		
P. agrestis	51.5–61.3		
Tree trunk 60–75 *L. rotundum*	60.7–68.9	13.9°C	38.3°C
L. blackwalli	64.9–75.1	12.4	
Field layer 70–80 *O. tridens*	63.5–72.1	10.3	38.3
Ground layer 85–100 *N. bimaculatum*	69.4–78.8	9.6	

Distribution and ecology

Distribution

The present distribution of a species is the result of many factors. Such factors include the evolutionary history of the species and its environment, its biology and ecology, its abilities to disperse and compete, and the present extent of its habitat or habitats. As far as harvestmen are concerned, the 'headquarters' of their distribution is in the humid tropics. In tropical rain forests their species diversity is high and in some forests their biomass may exceed that of the spiders. But their species diversity decreases much more strongly in colder and drier climates than in the case of spiders. Our harvestman fauna of just 23 species compares poorly with the total of c. 630 species of spiders in Great Britain.

Species of harvestmen generally do not have an extensive distribution (with some notable exceptions below). Compared with spiders they have weak powers of dispersal. They lack the aerial mobility of small and young spiders which may travel on gossamer silk threads to distant and isolated lands (a method known as 'ballooning'). For the purely terrestrial harvestmen seas present a serious barrier to dispersal.

Widely distributed species

Mitopus morio (p. 74) is the most outstanding example of a species with great powers of dispersal and broad ecological tolerances. It occurs throughout the Palaearctic Region (N. Africa, Europe and Asia north of Himalaya) and has colonized most of the Arctic including many of the islands where often it is the only species of harvestman. Its habitats range from broad-leaved woodland to tundra.

The British fauna also includes the two other notable species which have exceptionally wide distributions in the world: *Phalangium opilio* (p. 78) and *Opilio parietinus* (p. 80). These adaptable species have increased their range largely in response to man's activities particularly transport, agriculture and urbanization. *P. opilio* is believed to have originated in S. E. European grasslands (Gruber & Hunt, 1973) but today it occurs throughout the Palaearctic, North America and in New Zealand. In most of its extended range it is characteristic of disturbed habitats. *O. parietinus* is believed (Gruber & Hunt, 1973) to have originated in Western Asia (Anatolia and Caucasia) but it now also occurs throughout much of Europe, North America and in Tasmania. It is closely associated with man (**synanthropic**); indeed it is the only species which inhabits central London. It has probably existed in this country for 200 years or more (Meade, 1855).

Restricted distributions

By comparison with the above, *Sabacon viscayanum ramblaianum* (p. 52), a recent discovery in south Wales (Abbott, 1982), has an extremely limited distribution. It was originally described (Martens, 1983) from the Pyrenees which remains its only other provenance (the **nominate** subspecies occurs in the Cantabrian Mts.). It is likely that the species and its subspecies are relicts in the process of contraction from a previously more extensive distribution. Throughout the Northern Hemisphere (Japan, E. Asia, Europe & N. America) all the species of *Sabacon* have local and disjunct distributions (Martens, 1983). However, C. Merrett (pers. comm.) expresses some doubt about the relict status of *Sabacon* in Wales. It appears to have an affinity there with old industrial workings and this might suggest introduction.

All the species on the British list occur also on the Continent of Europe. For many years the possibility existed that *Paroligolophus meadii* (p. 68) was an endemic species confined to the British Isles. However, its discovery on Guernsey in 1955 suggested that this was less likely and indeed, Martens (1978) has now recorded it from northern Spain (Cantabrian Mts).

Introductions

It is much more likely that new additions to the British list will come as introductions from abroad than as discoveries of new indigenous or endemic species. One might even speculate that *Opilio canestrinii* (Thorell) could be the next addition. From southern Europe this species has recently expanded its range north westwards occurring mostly in man-made habitats (Gruber, 1984). Today it is frequent around houses and gardens in West Germany and Denmark. It is distinguished from the British species of *Opilio* by the absence of any stout tubercles on the palpal femur and by the presence of two conspicuous grooves on the penis shaft.

To date, *Dicranopalpus ramosus* (p. 92) is our only known example of an immigrant from Europe in modern times. First discovered at Bournemouth by E. Rix in 1957 it now has many thriving colonies most of which are near the south coast from Wales to East Anglia (Map 22, p. 109). Gardens are a favourite habitat and it has been noticed that *Dicranopalpus* is frequently associated with exotic trees and shrubs (D. G. Brown, pers. comm.). It is probable that the species entered the country on garden shrubs, possibly via eggs laid in the accompanying soil. Rambla (1986) gives a full account of the species together with a map which shows the east coast of Spain to be the centre of distribution.

The Biological Recording Scheme

The known distribution of harvestmen in the British Isles is given in this volume on separate maps (p. 103–9).

The records are processed and stored at the Biological Records Centre, Monks Wood and have been retrieved on 10 km squares (Sankey, 1988). They incorporate, as far as possible, those given by Bristowe (1949) and others who earlier recorded distribution by vice-counties.

Undoubtedly species occur in many of the squares which are at present blank. Partly this is a consequence of insufficient collecting but, of course, the widespread destruction of natural habitats in this country means that many squares will always remain blank. However, there is still much survey work to be done. Records cards should be submitted with full grid reference and detailed habitat data. Those interested in contributing to the Recording Scheme are invited to contact the Biological Records Centre, Institute of Terrestrial Ecology, Monks Wood Experimental Station, Abbotts Ripton, Huntingdon PE17 2LS.

It is also a good idea to join the British Arachnological Society. Membership Secretary: R. G. Snazell, Institute of Terrestrial Ecology, Furzebrook Research Station, Wareham, Dorset, BH20 5AS.

Ecology

The ecology of harvestmen, i.e. their relationship to the environment, is influenced by factors such as:

(1) habitat structure and density
(2) water relations
(3) temperature preferences or tolerances
(4) food availability and choice
(5) soil type

Probably the most important factor in Britain is habitat structure and density, i.e. the amount of space (Adams, 1984). A correlation is now recognised to exist between the length of leg in the various species and the structure and density of their habitat. Trogulids for example, sluggish forms with the shortest legs, invariably live at the soil/plant interface, under stones or in dense litter. By contrast, *Leiobunum rotundum* (p. 94), which has the longest legs, moves freely over grassland, hedgerows, tree trunks and woodland canopy. Between the extremes of these two forms the relationship of space to leg length generally holds good.

Habitat structure

Habitat structure is classified by standard according to the following horizons:

(1) ground layer
(2) herbaceous or field layer
(3) understorey or shrub layer
(4) tree or canopy layer

Synanthropic species fit into an additional category: man-made habitats. The micro-habitats found under stones and fallen wood, though classified as 'ground layer', are often used for shelter by relatively long legged species, e.g. *Opilio saxatilis* (p. 82).

25

Species characteristic of the above horizons are grouped as follows:

(a) ground layer – usually up to about 10 cm above soil surface but depth variable in leaf litter.

Trogulus tricarinatus
Anelasmocephalus cambridgei
Nemastoma bimaculatum
Mitostoma chrysomelas
Homalenotus quadridentatus

Sabacon v. ramblaianum
Lophopilio palpinalis
Lacinius ephippiatus
Paroligolophus meadii
Oligolophus tridens

Also present are the young stages of many species which with maturity move into higher horizons.

(b) herbaceous or field layer – e.g. rank grass, heather and surface of leaf litter.

Mitopus morio
Mitopus m. var ericaeus
Oligolophus tridens
Paroligolophus agrestis
Lophopilio palpinalis
Lacinius ephippiatus

Opilio saxatilis
Rilaena triangularis
Leiobunum rotundum
Leiobunum blackwalli
Nelima gothica
Phalangium opilio

(c) & (d) shrub layer, tree layer and old stone walls

Oligolophus hanseni
Paroligolophus agrestis
Mitopus morio
Megabunus diadema

Dicranopalpus ramosus
Leiobunum rotundum
Leiobunum blackwalli
Phalangium opilio

(e) synanthropic habitats (man-made and disturbed)

Odiellus spinosus
Paroligolophus agrestis
Dicranopalpus ramosus

Phalangium opilio
Opilio parietinus
Leiobunum rotundum

In a study of four woodlands in S.E. England (Adams, 1984), the habitat preferences of a number of species were brought into finer focus in terms of structure and density. It was found that leaves of different sizes, e.g. sweet chestnut (18 × 10 cm) and beech (10 × 7 cm), resulted in woodland litter of differing density and compressibility. The different types of litter were in turn favoured by different species of harvestmen. For example, the short-legged Nemastoma bimaculatum was associated with the dense beech litter while the longer legged Lacinius ephippiatus was most frequent in the chestnut litter with its larger inter-leaf spaces.

Water relations

Harvestmen are more susceptible to dehydration than most other arachnids. To minimize water losses many species, particularly those in upper horizons, are more active at night than during the day. The need for a humid habitat is a significant ecological factor and it is probably the most important limiting factor in the Mediterranean Region for example. Harvestmen there are always much more common in and around shady, damp water-courses, dark places and humid thickets. Also there is a strong tendency to reach maturity in the spring rather than during the hot, dry summer. In Britain humidity is a less obvious constraint but nevertheless many species are more common in damp, rather than dry woods.

The young stages are the most vulnerable to dehydration. They remain among the litter or within the sufficiently humid depths of the herbaceous horizon. A marked tendency for later instars and mature individuals to ascend the vegetational zones was first noted by Todd (1949). For example, *Lacinius ephippiatus* (p. 70) was found to move upward in the litter while *Mitopus morio* (p. 74) (depending on the habitat) moved from litter to the foliage of trees. In many species this is partly a diurnal migration, for example, *Leiobunum rotundum* (p. 94) is most active at night when it may climb well up tree trunks and walls. Harvestmen in open or man-made habitats are almost exclusively nocturnal and they shelter in micro-habitats during the day, e.g. *Opilio parietinus* (p. 80). *Paroligolophus meadii* (p. 68) does in fact occur in dry habitats such as open grassland but invariably it is found at the soil/plant interface. Todd (1949) gave figures for humidity and temperature preferences determined in the laboratory and these correspond well with the natural ecology observed in the field (Table 2; p. 21).

Temperature and other factors

The falling off in species diversity from southern to northern Britain is part of the overall trend from the tropics to the poles noted already. All but one of our species occur in Sussex but only eleven species are found north of the Great Glen in Scotland. Temperature must be an important factor here but, of course, the picture is complicated by the scarcity of woodland habitat in the north. Possibly our best example of a temperature dependant species is the south west European *Odiellus spinosus*. The distribution northwards of this species does appear to be limited by temperature or rather, a lack of sufficient warmth. In this country its range extends to the midlands (Map 13, p. 106) where it reaches the same latitude (53°N) as it does on the Continent (Holland). On the Continent *O. spinosus* occurs in grasslands, heathlands, dunes and stony places (Spoek, 1963). Here it behaves as a synanthropic species occurring in gardens and on waste ground; possibly it has only a relatively recent history in this country. Todd (1949) found that its temperature preference is high (16.3°C) as is its 'heat death point' (45°C). Most other species die at about 38°–39°C.

Many species are extremely cold tolerant and cold, by itself, can hardly be identified as a factor affecting communities in this country. A number of British species pass the winter as juveniles or adults. In Nemastomatidae the two indigenous species inhabit the high mountain tops as well as the lowlands. We have found torpid specimens of *Mitostoma chrysomelas* (p. 44) in January which could be re-awakened by gently breathing on them. Taken indoors they became active and mated just as if spring had arrived.

If habitat structure and density, water relations and temperature are the generally important factors affecting the ecology of harvestmen, other parameters such as food availability and soil type are important only in certain cases. Many authors (e.g. Todd, 1949 & 1950, Bristowe, 1949, Phillipson, 1960a, Edgar, 1971 and Adams, 1984) have found that most harvestmen are avid feeders with catholic tastes which will attack any available small, soft-bodied insects. Thus as generalist feeders food is not normally a critical factor. However, this is not to say that a harvestman's diet may not be dominated by particular types of prey. For example, *Nematoma bimaculatum* (p. 42) is likely to subsist largely on Collembola and small Diptera because these form the dominant prey in its dense micro-habitat. The young, ground-dwelling stage of *Mitopus morio* (p. 74) feed on similar prey but mature specimens in upper horizons are likely to find and consume many heteropteran and homopteran nymphs. In the case of the trogulids one may observe that they occur only where the soils are derived from limestone. As they are specialist feeders on snails, creatures which require calcium in the soil, the distribution of trogulids may actually reflect that of their prey.

The fossil record of Opiliones

Opiliones have a long but mostly rather sparse fossil record. The majority of known fossils belong to the suborder Palpatores and only two are described as Laniatores. However, while the long-legged forms (i.e. Palpatores) are readily identifiable as opilionid fossils, recent studies (P. A. Selden, pers comm.) suggest that the shorter-legged forms may in the past have been assigned erroneously to other arachnid orders. In a useful review of fossil opilionids by Cokendolpher (1986), Palpatores are described as numerous in Tertiary deposits (18–28 million years old) e.g. Baltic Amber, Dominican Republic Amber and the Florissant Formation of Colorado. Mesozoic arachnids (65–225 m.y.) are rare; only one opilionid has been described (Lower Cretaceous, Australia). Palaeozoic opilionids (older than 225 m.y.) are known from five described species in two families; it is remarkable how closely they resemble modern forms.

The oldest fossil opilionid in the world was in fact found recently in Great Britain (Wood *et al.*, 1985). It was collected by Mr. Stanley Wood from the East Kirkton Limestone near Edinburgh. The limestone belongs to the Brigantian stage of the Lower Carboniferous and is between 330 and 340 million years old. The specimen is almost certainly a member of the Palpatores and closely resembles the modern *Leiobunum* in shape and dimensions. Other Carboniferous opilionids are known from the Coal Measures of France and Illinois (Petrunkevitch, 1949).

The East Kirkton Limestone has also produced plants, myriapods, scorpions and terrestrial amphibians and deserves mention as one of the earliest sites to produce most of the components of a modern terrestrial ecosystem (Milner, 1985). As most of the major arachnid orders are known from the Devonian, the period preceding the Carboniferous, it is highly probable that diversification of the group, including the evolution of the Opiliones, took place prior to the Carboniferous.

Practical methods

Collection

Harvestmen may be collected in woods, heaths, meadows, gardens and other habitats by most of the methods known to spider-hunters and entomologists. 'Sweeping' and 'beating' the vegetation are effective methods above the ground; on the ground collections may be made by searching vegetation, stones and logs, by pitfall trapping and by litter sampling (see Fig. 7). Beating with a beating tray or an upturned umbrella is a favourite method for collecting specimens from the foliage of trees and bushes (Fig. 7C). The foliage is beaten with a stick causing the harvestmen to drop down; with this method they are less likely to be damaged than when sweeping.

Pitfall trapping is an efficient means of collecting ground-living harvestmen; for the purposes of supplying ecological data it is probably the most objective method of collecting as catches should be less affected by the collector's personal performance. Pitfall traps (Fig. 7A) are best made from small plastic beakers one-third filled with 50% ethylene glycol (with a trace of detergent to reduce surface tension). Commercial 'anti-freeze' is not recommended because catches are likely to develop an unpleasant smell. A bulb-planting tool used in suitable ground makes a neat hole for the beaker. Traps should be emptied and replenished at least weekly; one beaker inside another makes the operation easier.

Litter sampling (Fig. 7D) may be done in the field, laboratory or home. Bagfuls of leaf litter, for example, can be turned out over a white sheet, preferably in the sun or under a lamp.

The litter may be placed in a sieve before shaking over the sheet; a sieve with about nine holes to the square inch is helpful in finding ground-living species such as trogulids. Small harvestmen which move out from the litter are most easily collected by a pooter (Fig. 7B). Specimens are sucked into the glass barrel and prevented from being drawn into the mouth by a piece of nylon stocking. Because of their nocturnal activity, searching at night with a torch can be most productive; leiobunids may themselves be attracted to the light of a mercury vapour lamp. They may also come to the entomologists' sugar patch.

Preservation and examination

Harvestmen may be killed and preserved in 70 or 80% ethyl alcohol (ethanol), or in colourless industrial methylated spirit (IMS),* preferably with a trace of

---

* *Note.* For a licence (no charge) to buy industrial methylated spirit for the preservation of biological material, apply to the nearest Customs & Excise Office. At the time of writing propylene phenoxetol requires no licence.

30

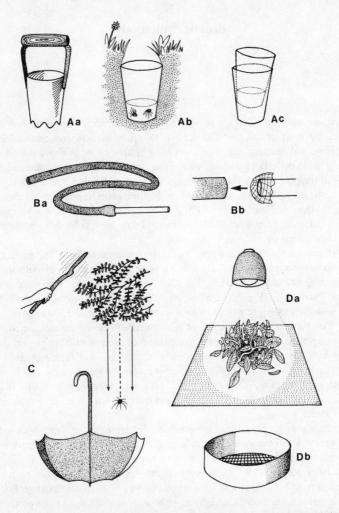

Fig. 7. Some methods of collection (also see text). A. Pitfall-trapping: Aa. Bulb-planting tool for extracting soil core; Ab. Pitfall-trap in situ, a small plastic beaker one-third filled with preservative; Ac. Using one beaker inside another. B. Simple aspirator or pooter: Ba. Rigid tube of aperture 5–10 mm and length approximately 10 cm fitted into flexible tubing of approximately 50 cm length; Bb. Fitting the tubes together with a piece of gauze or nylon, taking care not to damage the mesh. C. Beating foliage with a stick and umbrella. D. Sorting litter: Da. Using a source of light over a white plastic sheet or newspaper; Db. Sieve (optional).

glycerine added to maintain suppleness and as an insurance against complete drying-out. S. J. Moore (pers. comm.) advises that a 10% solution of propylene glycol in spirit will considerably reduce the problem of evaporation and help to keep the specimens supple. Alternatively, a water-based solution of 1% propylene phenoxetol (mixed with hot water to prevent formation of a colloid) is an effective preservative after first fixing the specimens in spirit for 24 hours. With 'P.P.' the problem of evaporation is very much reduced; the specimens remain soft and in a condition suitable for dissection. Formalin (40% formaldehyde) is not recommended as a preservative. Furthermore, specimens cannot be preserved by pinning and air drying though they can be successfully freeze dried for display purposes.

Specimens are best kept in glass, or clear plastic, tubes with polythene closures (Fig. 8C); a number of tubes may be stored together in a jar of preservative. Each tube should contain only one species, the specimens should not be crowded and, ideally, they should originate from a single locality. Labelling of the tubes is most important. The labels, placed *inside* the tubes, should be written in water and spirit proof ink or printed. The data on the label should be as detailed as possible and include the date, habitat, locality and collector's name (Fig. 8B). It is bad practice to have the data only in a note book, which may get lost. Printed record cards are available for the recording of harvestmen by the 10 km grid system (see p. 23); for this purpose the map reference is required.

If a dissection of genitalia is made, the excised parts may be mounted on a cavity slide, with a cover glass, using 60% lactic acid as a clearing and temporary mounting medium (Fig. 8A). Probably the dissection will require a sharp scalpel and needles; occasionally it is possible to squeeze the male genitalia out through the genital operculum or draw it out with fine forceps. Sometimes specimens are found with the penis already extruded. Genitalia on a slide may be rotated under the microscope by carefully sliding the coverglass. Such a temporary mount will keep for some weeks. A permanent slide mount can be made using Canada balsam or a mixture of gum arabic and chloral hydrate (e.g. Berlese's fluid).

Other than when mounted on a slide, separated genitalia may be accommodated in a stoppered micro-vial inside the glass tube (Fig. 8C). The micro-vial should not be allowed to move about and damage the specimens. A partition inside the tube may be made by a wad of tightly packed tissue paper. Loosely fitting cotton wool is disastrous for snagging the tarsal claws. To send tubes of harvestmen by post, the minimum amount of preservative should be used; any empty spaces may be filled by tissue paper.

Specimens of harvestmen should be examined in a petri-dish under alcohol or phenoxytol. A stereoscopic (dissecting) microscope with a wide field of view and a variable (zoom) magnification is best for gross anatomical views. Slide mounts of genitalia should be examined under a high-power compound microscope.

Laboratory culture

Live harvestmen are not difficult to keep in captivity. On a small scale, one or two individuals may be kept in a covered petri-dish with a constantly moist piece of filter paper on the bottom and a leaf or two, under which they can creep. Much more interesting, however, is a larger vivarium holding ten or more specimens in which mating, oviposition and hatching can be studied. For this purpose any transparent, covered container, perhaps 30 cm × 15 cm × 15 cm, would be suitable. A layer of moist sand, into which a vessel of drinking water is sunk, should be included together with something suitable as a resting place (Fig. 8E). In a bare box, harvestmen are likely to lay their eggs in the drinking trough and to avoid this a small tray of damp soil or sand with a central stone should be provided. The eggs may be left to hatch undisturbed or they may be dug up to watch their progress using Guenthal's Method (Fig. 8D). The container should never be left in direct sunlight.

The tendency of the newly hatched young to die at the third or fourth instar has been overcome by Klee and Butcher (1968) who attributed it to the constancy of humidity in a closed container. If the container's cover can be safely removed for a period each day, the relative humidity can alternate between 40 and 90% and much more closely resemble the conditions in nature. Klee & Butcher were in this way able to successfully rear *Phalangium opilio* from egg to adult.

Harvestmen accept a wide range of food and it is unnecessary to spend much time finding living creatures for them. Most forms of raw meat with some fat and any yeast tablets plus dried egg, wholemeal flour etc., will suffice as a basic diet. However, over a long period, the addition of freshly killed small insects such as *Drosophila* is recommended. Todd (1950) used cultures of psocids and the larvae of the flour beetle *Tribolium confusum* to supplement the diet. Water, of course, is essential.

33

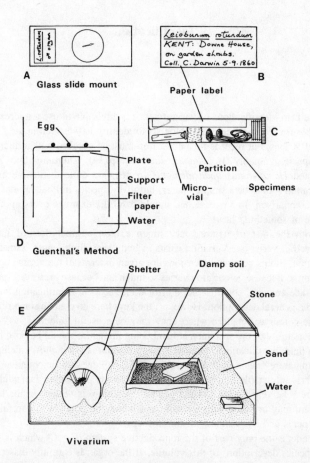

Fig. 8. Preservation and culture (also see text). A. Labelled glass slide suitable for mounting genitalia. B. Essential data on paper label written with permanent, water or spirit proof ink or typewritten. C. Glass tube (6 cm × 1 cm with plastic closure) containing preservative, label, specimens and, if required, tissue paper partition to separate glass micro-vial (containing dissected parts) from specimens which could be damaged. D. Guenthal's Method: apparatus for observing the development of eggs and comprising constantly moistened filter paper draped over a small glass plate supported by a pillar. E. Vivarium: fish tank or large lunch box with sandy floor, water supply, shelter or resting place and tray of damp soil with stone or tile as a suitable place for the live harvestmen to lay eggs.

Identification

To make firm identifications of harvestmen it is advisable to use a microscope. It is possible for experienced opilionologists to identify harvestmen in the field, say with a 10× lens, but records for publication must be checked with a microscope. Some species, notably *Megabunus diadema* (p. 84), *Dicranopalpus ramosus* (p. 92) and *Homalenotus quadridentatus* (p. 56), are quite distinctive and their identification should be a simple matter, but many species in Phalangiidae require careful comparison. In any case one should carefully examine every specimen in the hope of something new!

As with the rest of nature, harvestmen exhibit a great deal of individual (intraspecific) variation. Variation exists in body size, limb length, armature and colouration. In this volume dimensions are given in terms of the normal upper and lower limits. Because colouration varies so much and because preserved specimens tend to fade anyway, colour is not a critical character in identification but only a part of the general description. However, the keys here do contain some references to saddle colour and pattern where they may be a useful guide.

The possibility of the specimen at hand being immature should be born in mind. As with field identifications, familiarity with the adults often allows identification of the immature ones though the young of Phalangiidae and Leiobunidae may be particularly intractable. Early instars are less strongly pigmented than adults, their limbs are relatively longer and the genital operculum is sealed. In the adult the operculum may be lifted with a needle and it may be possible to carefully draw out the penis and ovipositor with fine forceps.

The penis is the only part of the reproductive system (Fig. 6) which is featured in the species descriptions of this volume. If the organ is carefully dissected out, mounted on a slide and examined under high hower, an unequivocal identification should be possible. The penis is not subject to wide intraspecific variation as are the somatic characters (*Preservation and Examination*, p. 29).

The keys and the species descriptions in the following pages refer to adult specimens in dorsal, lateral or ventral view. When using the keys it is advisable to consider the alternative part of the couplet even if the characters appear to fit the first part. In the species descriptions particular attention should be given to the characters mentioned under Diagnosis.

Systematics

Suborders of Opiliones

Three suborders of Opiliones are currently recognized worldwide:

1. CYPHOPHTHALMI Simon, 1879 'mite harvestmen'
A primitive group in which the members resemble the opiliocarid mites. The first pair of legs are longest, the eyes are absent and the openings of the odoriferous glands are placed on horns. Reproduction involves the production of a spermatophore; copulation does not occur as in other opilionids (van der Hammen, 1985). Approximately 50 species are known worldwide; neither of the two European species occurs in Britain. The group is considered by Savory (1977) to justify the rank of an order separate to that of Opiliones but Van der Hammen (1985) rejects this.

2. LANIATORES Thorell, 1876 'short legged harvestmen'
Probably the largest subdivision of the Opiliones but found mostly in tropical and subtropical regions. The second pair of legs is longest and, with few exceptions, eyes are present. The basal segments (coxae) of the first three pairs of legs touch at the midline. The openings of the odoriferous glands are not set on horns. The pedipalps have, characteristically, a large terminal claw which works against the tarsus as a grasping organ. The tibia and tarsus of the pedipalp usually possess two rows of long-spined tubercles. In central Europe there are just eight known species (in three families) (Martens, 1978). In southern Africa, Australia and New Zealand this suborder is dominant. In Central and South America, laniatorids of the families Cosmetidae and Gonyleptidae are abundant and often brightly coloured.

The laniatorid *Boeorix manducus* (family Assamiidae) is known from a hothouse in the Royal Botanic Gardens, Kew (Hillyard, 1981). However, this is an accidental importation, probably from southern Asia, and as it exists here only in an artificial environment it is not considered by us to be a genuine member of the British fauna.

3. PALPATORES Thorell, 1876
As in Laniatores the second pair of legs is longest but the coxae of the first three pairs of legs do not meet at the mid-line. The pedipalp claw is small or lacking and when present is not used as a grasping organ. The pedipalp tibia and tarsus may possess tubercles but they are never arranged in two rows. This suborder is distributed throughout the world; in the north temperate zone (North America, Europe and Asia) it is dominant. Palpatores are also abundant in the tropics and subtropics but much reduced in the south temperate zone. Eight families occur in Europe of which six are represented in Britain:

Nemastomatidae	2 species
Trogulidae	2 species
Sabaconidae	1 species (a subspecies)
Sclerosomatidae	1 species
Phalangiidae	13 species
Leiobunidae	4 species

The classification adopted here differs in part from that of Martens in his monograph of the European opilionid fauna (1978). In the case of the family Phalangiidae, Martens included five subfamilies: Phalangiinae, Oligolophinae, Gyantinae, Sclerosomatinae and Leiobuninae. However, Silhavy (1961), Shear (1982) and others including ourselves prefer to accord the rank of family to the last two groups, i.e. Sclerosomatidae and Leiobunidae. This position is justified on the grounds of their strong morphological identities though it is acknowledged that male genitalic characters may be arranged in a series (Martens, 1986) to support the retention of the taxa as subfamilies.

With the removal of Sclerosomatidae and Leiobunidae from Phalangiidae, as outlined above, the position of the subfamily Gyantinae within Phalangiidae becomes anomalous. Possessing a palpal claw with pectinations, it no longer rests comfortably in Phalangiidae, where the palpal claw is otherwise always smooth, in distinction from the Leiobunidae where the claw is pectinate. The structure of the palpal claw, i.e. pectinate or not, is considered to be a valid phylogenetic character in Opiliones. Other characters previously used to define the above groups within Phalangiidae, such as the presence or absence of marginal denticles on the coxae and the presence or absence of a ventral spine on the basal segment of the chelicera, have been found to be equivocal and not valid phylogenetically. Therefore, on this basis, the Gyantinae is here grouped together with the nominate subfamily (Leiobuninae) in the family Leiobunidae. The close relationship of Leiobuninae and Gyantinae was recognized by Martens (1978: p. 356). The three other families on the British list are almost universally recognized.

The 24 taxa in six families which currently form the British list are arranged as follows on page 37. Where names have changed in conformity with Martens (1978) the former name, as given in the 1974 edition of this *Synopsis* (Sankey & Savory, 1974), appears also. Two new taxa have recently been added: *Sabacon viscayanum ramblaianum* Martens 1982 (p. 52) and *Mitopus morio* var. *ericaeus* Jennings 1982 (p. 76).

Leiobunum tisciae Avram 1968 is reported (Martens, 1978) to have been found in Derbyshire in 1975. Our efforts to confirm this report have been unsuccessful and we do not feel justified in placing this species on the British list.

In the 1974 edition of this *Synopsis* it was pointed out that *Astrobunus scoticus* Roewer 1957 had no place in the British fauna. We wish to add that we can find no evidence that such a species exists anywhere.

Classification of British species of Harvestmen

Order OPILIONES Sundevall, 1833
  Suborder Palpatores Thorell, 1876
    Family Nemastomatidae Simon, 1879
        Nemastoma bimaculatum (Fabricius, 1775)
        Mitostoma chrysomelas (Hermann, 1804)
    Family Trogulidae Sundevall, 1833
        Trogulus tricarinatus (Linnaeus, 1767)
        Anelasmocephalus cambridgei (Westwood, 1874)
    Family Sabaconidae Dresco, 1970
        Sabacon viscayanum ramblaianum Martens, 1983
    Family Sclerosomatidae Šilhavý, 1961
        Homalenotus quadridentatus (Cuvier, 1795)
    Family Phalangiidae Simon, 1879
      Subfamily Oligolophinae Banks 1893
        Oligolophus tridens (C. L. Koch, 1836)
        Oligolophus hanseni (Kraepelin, 1896)
        Paroligolophus agrestis (Meade, 1855) = *Oligolophus agrestis*
        Paroligolophus meadii (O.P.-C., 1890) = *Oligolophus meadii*
        Lacinius ephippiatus (C. L. Koch, 1835)
        Odiellus spinosus (Bosc, 1792) = *Oligolophus (Odiellus) spinosus*
        Mitopus morio (Fabricius, 1799)
        Mitopus morio variety *ericaeus* Jennings, 1962
      Subfamily Phalangiinae Simon 1879
        Phalangium opilio Linnaeus, 1758
        Opilio parietinus (Degeer, 1778)
        Opilio saxatilis C. L. Koch, 1839
        Megabunus diadema (Fabricius, 1779)
        Rilaena triangularis (Herbst, 1799) = *Platybunus triangularis*
        Lophopilio palpinalis (Herbst, 1799) = *Oligolophus palpinalis*
    Family Leiobunidae Šilhavý, 1961
      Subfamily Gyantinae Šilhavý, 1946
        Dicranopalpus ramosus (Simon, 1909) = *Dicranopalpus caudatus*
      Subfamily Leiobuninae Banks, 1893
        Leiobunum rotundum (Latreille, 1798)
        Leiobunum blackwalli Meade, 1861
        Nelima gothica Lohmander, 1945 = *Nelima silvatica* (part)

38

Key to the Families of British Harvestmen (adults)

1. Legs 1 and 3 clearly longer than the body; legs 2 and 4 at least 1.5 times the length of the body

.... **3**

Legs 1 and 3 not or scarcely longer than body; legs 2 and 4 not or scarcely more than 1.5 times the length of the body

.... **2**

2. Front edge of cephalothorax produced into a 'hood' (arrowed) covering the mouthparts. Integument, except mouthparts and leg tarsi, usually covered with earth particles (2 species)

....TROGULIDAE (p. 46)

Front edge of cephalothorax without a hood but with a single median spine (arrowed). Posterior of abdoman with four blunt projections (arrowed) (1 species)

....SCLEROSOMATIDAE (p. 55)

3. Tarsus (arrowed) of pedipalp longer than tibia and with a terminal claw

.... 5

Tarsus of pedipalp shorter than tibia and without a terminal claw 4

4. Tarsus (arrowed) of pedipalp markedly short and swollen presenting a 'boxing glove' appearance. Both tarsus and tibia thickly covered with spines. Tarsal claw rudimentary or absent (1 species)

....SABACONIDAE (p. 52)

Pedipalp generally slender or very slender. Under high magnification many setae on pedipalp are seen to be 'club-shaped' (Figs. 9B & C and 10A) (2 species)

....NEMASTOMATIDAE (p. 40)

5. Terminal claw of pedipalp with pectination (high magnification) (arrowed). Armature (tendency to form tubercles on body and appendages) poorly developed (4 species)

....LEIOBUNIDAE (p. 90)

Terminal claw of pedipalp without pectination (arrowed). Armature usually well developed (13 species)

....PHALANGIIDAE (p. 58)

Family NEMASTOMATIDAE

Nemastomatids are small harvestmen, their body length is usually less than 5 mm. In the two genera which occur in Britain the colouration is either blackish (*Nemastoma*) or pale brown (*Mitostoma*). The carapace and tergites 1–5 are fused into a single, hard scutum. In *Mitostoma* the dorsum has an elaborate pattern of tubercles. The eyes of nemastomatids are raised on a distinct ocularium but there is no trident. The supra-cheliceral lamella is strongly indented unlike that in any other family. The openings of the odoriferous glands are not visible from above.

The pedipalp may be much longer than the body but the palpal tarsus is always shorter than the tibia unlike that in Phalangiidae and Leiobunidae. The pedipalp lacks a terminal claw but is well supplied with capitate hairs which occur in no other family. Like sabaconids, the male chelicerae have cheliceral glands with prominent apophyses; sexual dimorphism may also occur in the form of the pedipalps. The legs may be relatively short or long. All leg coxae are immovable but are distinctly separated. The maxillary lobe of coxa 2 is not developed and all legs lack accessory spiracles. The labium is small.

The ovipositor is short and without segmentation but has rings of setae. The penis corpus and glans are in a more or less straight line; the glans is set with stout denticles. The penis corpus is markedly swollen at the base. Nemastomatids occur mostly in the ground layer. The family comprises about a dozen genera found in Europe, northern Africa, western North America and Japan. In Britain there are two species placed in two genera.

Key to the species of Nemastomatidae (adults)

1. Legs long, leg 2 five or more times length of body. Dorsal surface of body yellow-brown with transverse continuous rows of tubercles (arrowed). Pedipalp longer than length of body

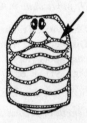

....*Mitostoma chrysomelas* (p. 44)

   Legs short, leg 2 less than four times length of body. Dorsal surface of body black with pair of pale spots (arrowed) anteriorly (rarely all black). Transverse rows of tubercles absent. Pedipalp shorter than length of body

....*Nemastoma bimaculatum* (p. 42)

Nemastoma bimaculatum (Fabricius)
(Fig. 9)

Phalangium bimaculatum Fabricius, 1775: *Systema Entomologiae:* 440
Nemastoma lugubre: Koch, 1836: *Die Arachniden* **3**: 71
N.lugubre-bimaculatum: Roewer, 1914: *Arch. Naturg.* **80A** (3): 134
N. lugubre-unicolor Roewer, 1914: *Arch. Naturg.* **80A** (30): 134
N. bimaculatum: Gruber & Martens, 1968: *Senckenberg. biol.* **49**: 149

Diagnosis: Trident and palpal claw absent. Pedipalp has 'capitate' setae (Fig. 5I).
Distinguished from *Mitostoma chrysomelas* (p. 44) by its blackish body with two
pale spots (rarely all black). Male chelicera and penis distinct (see below and
Figs. 9D, E & F).

Body length: male 2.0–2.5 mm, female 2.3–2.8 mm

Length of second leg: 5.5–8.5 mm

Body (Fig. 9A) mostly black or dark brown. Dorsal surface of cephalothorax with
two, almost square, silvery white patches. Dorsal shield of cepholothorax and
abdominal tergites 1–5 fused into a hard, sclerotized scutum; entire surface
granulate. Tergites 6–8 (free tergites) sclerotized but separated by pale
membranous integument, the extent of which depends upon presence of eggs or
state of nutrition. Ocularium near anterior margin, rather low, much wider than
long, pale on top and covered in small denticles. Openings of odoriferous glands
not visible. Supra-cheliceral lamella strongly indented. Sternites 4–7 as tergites
6–8, sclerotized and discrete.

Chelicerae rather small, dark. Sexually dimorphic: basal segment in male has a
cheliceral gland in the form of a prominent, antero-dorsal apophysis (Fig. 9D),
absent in female.

Pedipalps slender, mostly dark; terminal claw absent. All segments from femur
to tarsus furnished with erect, 'capitate' setae (Figs. 9B, C). Pedipalps somewhat
differently shaped in the two sexes; in particular the male tibia has a prominent
postero-dorsal boss (Fig. 9C), absent in female.

Legs short, dark brown but tarsi and metatarsi less dark; femoral bases with pale
constrictions.

Penis (Fig. 9E) swollen at base; glans furnished with eight acute, tooth-like
denticles on each side (Fig. 9F).

Occurrence. A ground-living species occurring in moss, leaf litter, under stones
and logs etc. Widespread throughout the British Isles including many off-shore
islands; it seems especially common in upland regions. The species often emerges
at night from its dense micro-habitats and may be readily collected in pitfall traps.
It is recorded as adult in all months of the year while the younger stages (which
lack the strong colouration) occur mostly during summer and autumn; one batch
of eggs may have an extended period of hatching. The life span of an individual
may be up to eighteen months (Phillipson, 1959).

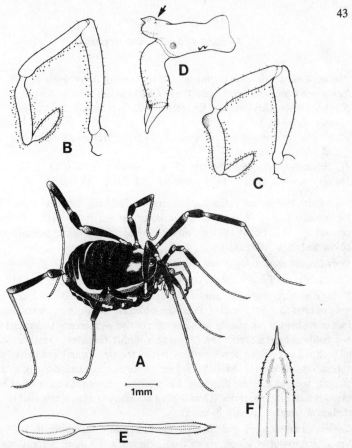

Fig. 9. *Nemastoma bimaculatum*. A. Whole animal; B. Outside lateral view of female left pedipalp; C. Outside lateral view of male left pedipalp; D. Outside lateral view of male left chelicera showing apophysis on basal segment (arrowed); E. Ventral, partly lateral, view of penis; F. Ventral view of glans penis.

Type locality is 'Anglia' (England). Recorded as very common in England by Meade (1855). (Map 2, p. 104). Abroad the species occurs from northern Iberia through France to Belgium and western Norway; in the Pyrenees up to 1500 m (Martens, 1978).

Remarks. The silvery white patches are occasionally absent. For such specimens Roewer (1914) described the subspecies *N. lugubre-unicolor* but this is regarded as only a variety by Sankey (1953a). The patches may fade in long-preserved specimens but usually reappear on drying. A specimen in which the dorsum was entirely white except for the free tergites is recorded from Box Hill, Surrey in September 1984.

The question of whether both *N. bimaculatum* and *N. lugubre* occur in the British Isles was finally settled by Gruber and Martens (1968) who found that only *bimaculatum*, clearly distinct from *lugubre*, occurred in Britain.

44

Mitostoma chrysomelas (Hermann)
(Fig. 10)

Phalangium chrysomelas Hermann, 1804: *Mémoire Apterologique:* 108
Nemastoma chrysomelas: Koch, 1839: *Übersicht des Arachnidensyst.* **2**: 38
N. chrysomelas chrysomelas: Kratochvil, 1934: *Acta Soc. Scient. nat.*
 moravosiles **9**: 8
Mitostoma chrysomelas chrysomelas: Roewer, 1951: *Senckenberg. biol.* **32**:
 142
M. chrysomelas confusum Spoek, 1963: *Zool. Verh. Leiden* **64**: 21
M. chrysomelas: Meijer, 1973: *Zool. Meded. Leiden* **46** (9): 117

Diagnosis: Trident and palpal claw absent. Pedipalp has 'capitate' setae (Fig. 5I). Distinguished from *Nemastoma bimaculatum* (p. 42) by its yellow-brown body crossed by rows of bifid and trifid tubercles. Male chelicera and penis distinct (see below and Figs. 10B, D).

Body length: male 1.5–1.8 mm, female 1.8–2.5 mm

Length of second leg: 13.0–18.0 mm

Body (Fig. 10A) yellowish brown. Dorsum rather flat-topped and decorated with rows of bifid or trifid tubercles (Fig. 5(J)) which enclose discrete areas. Dorsal surface of cephalothorax usually with a pattern of five such areas. Abdominal tergites 1–5 outlined by transverse rows forming a further five areas. Smaller, scattered tubercles occur within areas particularly in female. Lateral margin of dorsum almost continuously marked by a line of tubercles. Ocularium near anterior margin, somewhat wider than long and blackish except for central strip between two rows of bifid tubercles. Openings of odoriferous glands not visible. Supracheliceral lamella strongly indented.

Chelicerae rather small and brownish black. Sexually dimorphic: male (Fig. 10B) has an antero-dorsal apophysis on basal segment and a postero-dorsal apophysis on distal segment. The apophyses are associated with the cheliceral gland, both are absent in female (Fig. 10C).

Pedipalps (Fig. 10A) brown, very long and slender, up to twice length of body. All segments from femur to tarsus covered with erect 'capitate' setae (Fig. 5(I)). Terminal claw absent.

Legs relatively long and slender, brown or pale brown. Femora, patellae and tibiae clothed with short setae but pale hairless annulations occur on femora (Fig. 10A).

Penis swollen at base; glans (Fig. 10D) bulbous and furnished with setae on dorsal and lateral surfaces.

Occurrence. A ground-living species occurring in moss, leaf litter, rough grass, under stones and logs, and in caves. Widespread throughout the British Isles; it is frequent in Scotland though apparently under-recorded. Not as common as *Nemastoma bimaculatum* but tends to be more gregarious. Adults have been recorded in most months of the year; young stages throughout the year. Meijer (1984) showed that reproduction and development may occur at any time of the year if conditions are favourable but individuals are not long lived.

45

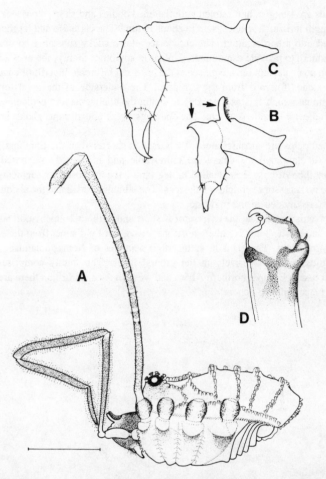

Fig. 10. *Mitostoma chrysomelas*. A. Lateral view of male body with pedipalp and femur plus patella of leg 1 (bar = 1 mm); B. Outside lateral view of left male chelicera showing apophyses on basal and distal segments (arrowed); C. Outside lateral view of female left chelicera; D. Lateral view of glans penis.

Type locality. Strasbourg, France; the first British record at Bradford (Meade, 1855). (Map 3, p. 104). Abroad the species ranges from France and Italy (Apennines) east to Poland, Yugoslavia and Romania, occurring up to 2000 m in Tatra Mts. It is local in Denmark and absent in Iberia and Scandinavia (Martens, 1978).

Remarks. This tiny and delicate species moves slowly and often appears to have difficulty controlling its long legs.

Family TROGULIDAE

Trogulids are sluggish harvestmen with flattened bodies and short, stout legs. The body length in British species is up to about 10 mm. The carapace and tergites 1–5 are fused into a hard scutum. The cuticle secretes a sticky substance so that soil grains adhere to provide camouflage. Unlike in any other family, the eyes are not raised on an ocularium but are placed at the base of a bifurcate 'hood', or cucullus, which extends forward from the carapace. The underside of the hood forms a camerostome which acts as a pocket enclosing the chelicerae and pedipalps. The supra-cheliceral lamella is absent. The openings of the odoriferous glands are not visible from above.

The pedipalps are inconspicuous; the tarsus is shorter than the tibia and lacks a terminal claw. All leg coxae are immovable and indistinctly separated; the maxillary lobe of coxa 2 is small. The leg tarsi have at most four segments and there are no accessory spiracles on the legs. The labium is small and the abdomonal sternites are divided in the mid line.

As in Nemastomatidae, the ovipositor is short and without segmentation but has rings of setae. The penis is rather short; the stylus, hardly distinct from the glans, is short and blunt. The glans lacks the stout denticles of Nemastomatidae.

Trogulids occur exclusively in the ground layer. The family comprises six genera found in Europe, northern Africa and western Asia. In Britain there are two species placed in two genera.

Key to the British Species of Trogulidae (adults)

1. Branches of the bifurcate hood semi-circular, the ends often fused by adhering soil particles and the space between bridged by long tubercles (Fig. 11C). Tarsi of legs 1 & 2 with two segments (arrowed and numbered). Body exceptionally flat, length 7-10 mm

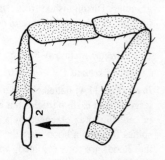

....*Trogulus tricarinatus* (p. 48)

Branches of the bifurcate hood short but with long tubercles radiating outwards (Fig. 12C). Tarsi of legs 1 & 2 with three segments (arrowed and numbered). Body slightly rounded, length 3-4 mm

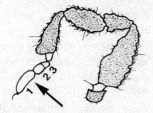

....*Anelasmocephalus cambridgei* (p. 50)

48

Trogulus tricarinatus (Linnaeus)
(Fig. 11)

Phalangium tricarinatum Linnaeus, 1767: Systema Naturae ed. 12: 1029
Opilio carinatum Herbst, 1799: Natursyst. Ungeflüg. Insekten 3: 13
Trogulus tricarinatus: Koch, 1839: Übersicht des Arachnidensyst. 2: 145

Diagnosis: Trident and palpal claw absent. Body remarkably flat, integument granular. Distinguished from Anelasmocephalus cambridgei by its larger size, the form of its hood and by careful comparison of the penes (see below and Figs. 11D, 12D).

Body length: male 5.0–8.0 mm, female 6.0–10.0 mm

Length of second leg: 7.0–8.0 mm

Body (Fig. 11A) flattened dorso-ventrally. Sandy brown, granular surface derived largely from earth particles but abdominal segmentation still discernible. Anterior of cephalothorax extended by a pair of semi-circular processes bridged by strong spines forming a hood over the mouthparts (Figs. 11B, C). The two branches of the hood are often joined apically by adhering earth particles (Fig. 11C). Ocularium absent; eyes at base of hood and separated by three times their diameter. Openings of odoriferous glands not visible.

Chelicerae small, brown, not granulate.

Pedipalps short and weak, brown, not granulate, terminal claw absent (Figs. 11A, B).

Legs relatively short and robust. Sandy and thickly granulate except for tarsus which is darker and not granulate. Tarsi 1 and 2 with two, tarsi 3 and 4 with three segments. Femur 1 with a series of spine-tipped tubercles and embedded in earth particles (Fig. 11A, entire leg 1).

Penis: corpus almost straight (Fig. 11D, compare Fig. 12D); stylus blunt, glans furnished with numerous setae.

Occurrence. A ground-living species confined to calcareous regions, mostly in the south, where it occurs in grass, leaf litter, under logs and stones etc. Most characteristically it occurs between the lower moist layer of fallen beech leaves and the soil; sieving is the best way to find it. Adults have been taken in all months of the year. In West Germany (Pabst, 1953) eggs are laid in October and November and again from March to May while hatching occurs mostly from May to July. Individuals may take up to three quarters of a year to pass through six moults and become adult. They may live for a total of three years. The young stages have a purplish colour, especially when freshly moulted, and are not normally covered with grains of soil.

Type locality. Dresden (East Germany). The first discovery in Britain was by the Rev. O. Pickard-Cambridge (1890) at Bloxworth, Dorset (an immature specimen). The first adult was found by Wallis Kew on the Warren at Folkestone, Kent in 1905. (Map 4, p. 104). Abroad the species occurs from France, Holland and Switzerland east to Poland and Bulgaria; it is local in Denmark and absent in

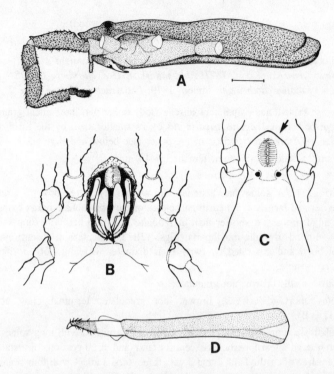

Fig. 11. *Trogulus tricarinatus*. A. Lateral view of body with pedipalp and leg 1 (bar = 1 mm); B. Ventral view of cephalothorax showing camerostome (receptacle for mouthparts); C. Dorsal view of cephalothorax showing hood (arrowed); D. Ventral, partly lateral, view of penis.

Scandinavia (Martens, 1978). It is introduced in North America (New York State, Muchmore, 1963).

Remarks. A difficult species to find even when sieving woodland litter on to a white sheet under a bright light. Usually it feigns death (catalepsy) and moves only after some minutes. Snails, abundant in calcareous regions, are an important part of the diet and empty shells are used for depositing eggs (Pabst, 1953). The possibility that two species of *Trogulus* exist in Great Britain is discussed by Martens (1988).

50

Anelasmocephalus cambridgei (Westwood)
(Fig. 12)

Trogulus cambridgii Westwood, 1874: *Thesaurus Ent. Oxoniensis:* 202
Anelasma sörenseni: Koch, 1877: *Abh. naturhist. Ges. Nürnberg* **6**: 195
Anelasmocephalus cambridgei: Simon, 1879: *Les Arachnides de France* **7**: 299

Diagnosis: Trident and palpal claw absent. Body rather flat, integument granular. Distinguished from *Trogulus tricarinatus* by its smaller size, by the form of its hood and by careful comparison of the penes (see below and Figs. 12D, 11D).

Body length: male 2.8–3.5 mm, female 3.0–4.0 mm

Length of second leg: 3.8–4.3 mm

Body (Fig. 12A) somewhat flattened dorso-ventrally. Grey-brown, granular surface derived largely from earth particles. Anterior of cephalothorax extended by a pair of processes, shorter than in *Trogulus* but furnished with long spines, forming a hood over the mouthparts (Figs. 12B, C). Ocularium absent; eyes at base of hood and separated by twice their diameter. Openings of odoriferous glands not visible.

Chelicerae small, brown, not granulate.

Pedipalps short and weak, brown, not granulate, terminal claw absent (Figs. 12A, B).

Legs relatively short and robust. Grey brown and furnished with long spines and setae embedded in earth particles except for tarsi (and distal portions of metatarsi) which are free of earth. Tarsi 1 and 2 with three, tarsi 3 and 4 with four segments (the first two segments are indistinctly separated). Fig. 12A shows entire leg 1 including tarsal segments.

Penis: corpus curved in lateral view (Fig. 12D, compare Fig. 11D); stylus blunt, glans furnished with setae but numbers fewer than in *Trogulus*.

Occurrence. A ground-living species usually found in calcareous regions where it occurs in grass, moss, leaf litter, under logs and stones etc. It appears to have a preference for rough grassland and semi-open woodland where the field layer is interspersed with leaf litter and moss; it is best collected by sieving or in pitfall traps. Adults occur in all months of the year and the immature stages mostly from May to October. On the Continent, Pabst (1953) records egg-laying in all months except December and January. Development through five moults to adulthood is shorter than in *Trogulus* but, similarly, individuals may live up to three years. Immatures are purplish in colour, especially when freshly moulted, and are not normally covered with grains of soil.

Type locality. Bloxworth, Dorset where the species was discovered by O. Pickard-Cambridge but described by Westwood (1874). (Map 5, p. 104) Abroad the species is distributed from northern Spain through France, Switzerland and Belgium to the River Elbe (West Germany); it is local in Holland (Martens, 1978).

Remarks. Like *Trogulus* this species exhibits catalepsy and is hard to find; however, it is much more frequent.

51

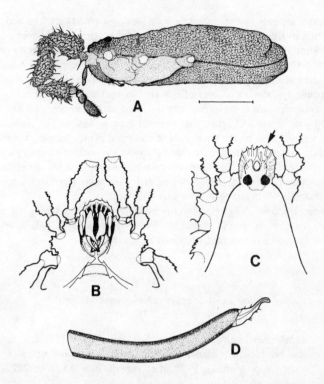

Fig. 12. *Anelasmocephalus cambridgei*. A. Lateral view of body with pedipalp and leg 1 (bar = 1 mm); B. Ventral view of cephalothorax showing camerostome (receptacle for mouthparts); C. Dorsal view of cephalothorax showing hood (arrowed); D. Lateral view of penis.

52

Family SABACONIDAE

Sabaconids are pale brown, rather delicate looking harvestmen. The body, up to 4 or 5 mm in length, is soft but a relatively rigid **scutum** may be formed by the combination of a number of dorsal elements. Prominent spines in rows occur all over the body and to a large extent on the appendages. The eyes are raised on an ocularium but a trident is absent. The supra-cheliceral lamella is inconspicuous. The openings of the odoriferous glands are not visible from above.

The pedipalps are conspicuous; the tibia and tarsus are swollen and thickly covered with spines and setae. The terminal claw is absent. The chelicerae are modified in the male by the possession of cheliceral glands forming a dorsal boss on the basal segment. The legs are relatively short and without accessory spiracles. The coxae are movable but the maxillary lobe on coxa 2 is not developed.

The ovipositor is short and not segmented. The penis resembles a spear, the glans somewhat flattened forming a keel structure.

Sabaconids inhabit the ground layer or occur in caves. The family has a highly disjunct distribution in the Northern Hemisphere; there is only one genus, *Sabacon*, which is represented in Britain by a subspecies.

Sabacon viscayanum ramblaianum Martens
(Fig. 13)

Sabacon vizcayaznus Dresco, 1952: *Ann. Soc. ent. France* **121**: 122
S. viscayanus ramblaianum Martens, 1983: *Senckenberg. biol.* **63** (3/4): 278
S. viscayanum subsp. Martens, 1983: *Senckenberg. biol.* **63** (3/4): 282

Diagnosis: Trident and palpal claw absent. Distinguished from all others by the form of the pedipalp: tarsus and tibia somewhat swollen and densely covered in spines and setae (Fig. 13A).

Body length: male 2.5–3.5 mm, female 3.4–4.6 mm

Length of second leg: 15.0–20.0 mm

Body (Fig. 13A) grey-brown on dorsum with whitish areas either side of ocularium, across last segments of cephalothorax (meso- & metapeltidium) and each abdominal tergite. A pair of prominent spines occurs in centre of metapeltidium (Fig. 13B). Ocularium twice as wide as long and approximately one half its length distant from front margin of cephalothorax. Ocularium mostly black but with central pale band in dorsal view; surface of ocularium smooth. Trident absent. Openings of odoriferous glands inconspicuous. Ventrum grey-brown and furnished with many stout hairs.

Chelicerae brown, relatively strong and furnished with many spines. Basal segment in male with dorsal boss (cheliceral gland, Fig. 13C). Boss parallel sided and provided with many spines. Basal segment without ventral spur.

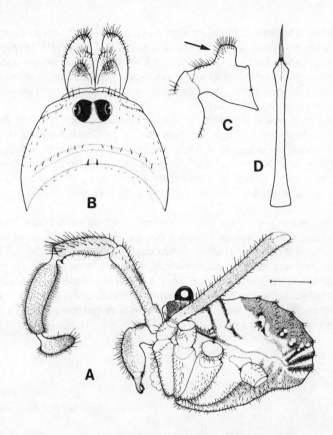

Fig. 13. *Sabacon viscayanum ramblaianum*. A. Lateral view of male body with pedipalp and femur of leg 1 (bar = 1 mm); B. Dorsal view of male cephalothorax with chelicerae; C. Outside lateral view of male chelicera (basal segment) showing dorsal boss (arrowed); D. Ventral view of penis (after Martens, 1982).

Pedipalps longer than body and with an unusual appearance (Fig. 13A). Femur and patella brown and furnished with many spines and setae. Tarsal claw absent. Male has a series of black disto-ventral tubercles on patella, first tubercle most prominent.

Legs brown, moderately long and stout, furnished with many spines. Femora, under high magnification, with irregular ridges (Fig. 13A).

Penis (Fig. 13D): corpus, glans and stylus in same plane; stylus one quarter the length of corpus.

Occurrence. The rarest and most localized harvestman in Great Britain. At present it is known from just a few sites in south Wales. It has been found in deep leaf litter in damp woodland and under debris at a woodland fringe; some of the sites are close to abandoned industrial works. Adults have been collected in late summer and autumn. Little is known about the life cycle or whether the harvestman over-winters as eggs, young or adults.

Type locality of the subspecies is Oloron, Basses-Pyrénées. The first British record was by Abbott (1981) in September 1980 at the Gower Peninsula (Map 6, p. 105). Abroad the subspecies occurs at a number of localities in the western and central Pyrenees (Martens, 1983). The genus may be described as a 'Tertiary relict'; its species are found in isolated parts of the Northern Hemisphere – Japan, Korea, central Asia, S.W. Europe, eastern and Western North America.

Remarks. On the basis of just one female specimen from south Wales, Martens (1983) made a provisional description under the name of *S. viscayanum* subsp. Since then, after receiving a male specimen sent by C. Merrett from Wales, Prof. Martens concluded that the subspecies is *ramblaianum* (pers. comm.).

To quote Merrett (1984) '*Sabacon* lies flat with legs extended; it can easily be overlooked due to its dark greyish hue and when disturbed will curl up and feign death. However, it can move rapidly and it is then that the curiously-shaped pedipalps show up to the naked eye'.

Family SCLEROSOMATIDAE

Sclerosomatids are short legged harvestmen with a tough, somewhat flattened body. The body length reaches about 4 or 5 mm. The dorsal surface is covered by a spiny scutum but the last three tergites (free tergites) lie on the ventral surface. Additional sclerites are present on the lateral surface of the abdomen. The eyes are raised on an ocularium. There is no trident but a large median spine projects from the anterior edge of the carapace (in *Homalenotus*). The supra-cheliceral lamella lacks tubercles. The openings of the odoriferous glands are not visible from above.

The pedipalps are short and the terminal claw is pectinate. The basal segment of the chelicera has a ventral spine. The labium is relatively small as is the maxillary lobe of the second leg coxa. The coxae are to some extent movable; the legs are without accessory spiracles.

The ovipositor is multi-segmented. The penis is rather simple; corpus, glans and stylus are held in a more or less straight line.

Sclerosomatids inhabit the ground layer. The family is a relatively small one with eight genera found in Europe, Asia and North Africa. Only one species occurs in Britain.

56

Homalenotus quadridentatus (Cuvier)
(Fig. 14)

Phalangium 4-dentatum Cuvier, 1795: *Magazin Encyclopédique* 1: 206
Homalenotus quadridentatus: Koch, 1839: *Über. des Arachnidensyst.* 2: 23

Diagnosis: Trident replaced by a single prominent tubercle. Palpal claw with pectination. Distinguished from all others by the series of tubercles on the dorsum, the last four of which are directed rearwards (Figs. 14A, B).

Body length: male 3.5–4.5 mm, female 4.0–5.0 mm

Length of second leg: 8.0–12.0 mm

Body sandy brown with a pattern, variable in intensity, of dark marks as in Fig. 14A. The four dark marks (central pair darkest) across each abdominal tergite, nos. 1–5, are each surmounted by a pale blunt tubercle; on posterior margin of dorsum (tergite 5) the four tubercles are directed rearwards. The last three tergites are on the ventral surface. Body flattened dorso-ventrally (Fig. 14B), integument tough and surface often encrusted with soil particles. Ocularium black, relatively small, almost twice as long as wide and provided with two rows of (usually) four modest tubercles. Front margin of cephalothorax with a single tubercle, usually very prominent and inclined at about 25°. Openings of odoriferous glands not visible from above. Ventrum brown with irregular dark spots.

Chelicerae small, shaped normally, dark brown and not granular. Basal segment has a ventral spur.

Pedipalps (Fig. 14B) relatively short; surface partly granular but tarsus furnished only with hairs. Ventral surface of femur and trochanter with a number of short, spine-tipped tubercles. Tarsal claw pectinate.

Legs sandy brown, relatively short and with a partly granular surface; granulation reduced on metatarsus and absent on tarsus. Prominent tubercles occur on dorsal surface of femora, trochanters and coxae. Fig. 14B shows entire legs 1 & 2.

Penis (Fig. 14C): in dorsal or ventral view, corpus, glans and stylus held in straight line.

Occurrence. Homalenotus is found predominantly south of a line from the Mersey to the Humber; it has also been recorded from Malham in Yorkshire. It occurs in the ground layer of woods, especially open beechwoods, and in calcareous grasslands. It should be looked for at the base of plant stems, in leaf litter and under logs and stones. Sieving is an effective way of finding it and it may also be collected in pitfall traps. Adults have been recorded in all months of the year. As the young are most numerous in late summer it is probable that the eggs are laid around June and July. The young are paler in colour than the adults and have no soil encrustation.

Type locality is unknown. The first British record was by Meade (1855) who discovered it at Hampden (Buckinghamshire). Map 7, p. 105. Abroad the species is distributed from northern Iberia through France, not quite reaching the Rhine. It occurs on the Azores but it is absent in the Mediterranean Basin. It ascends to 1800 m in the Pyrenees (Martens, 1978).

57

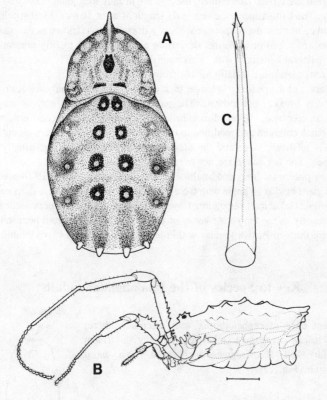

Fig. 14. *Homalenotus quadridentatus*. A. Dorsal view of body; B. Lateral view of body with pedipalp and legs 1 & 2 (bar = 1 mm); C. Ventral view of penis.

Family PHALANGIIDAE

Phalangiids are typical harvestmen, the legs are usually long and the body soft and leathery. The British species have a body length of up to 10 mm. Most species are brown in colour and many specimens show a dorsal pattern known as the 'saddle'. The eyes are raised on a distinct ocularium and a trident is usually present. The supra-cheliceral lamella is with or without median denticles. The openings of the odoriferous glands are usually visible from above.

The tarsus of the pedipalp is longer than the tibia and a terminal claw is present; the claw is smooth, not toothed. The palpal patella and tibia may or may not possess an apophysis. Sexual dimorphism may be evident in the chelicerae which can be much enlarged and modified in the male; cheliceral glands are absent. The labium is relatively large and the maxillary lobe on leg coxa 2 is usually well developed. The leg coxae are not fixed.

The ovipositor is long and multi-segmented. The penis is shaft-like with a distinct glans held at an angle with the corpus; the stylus resembles a short needle.

Phalangiids inhabit all vegetational layers. Approximately 30 genera occur in the world, mostly in the temperate zones of the northern and southern hemispheres. There are thirteen British species within ten genera placed in two subfamilies.

Key to Species of the Phalangiidae (adults)

1. Front edge of cephalothorax with essentially three, closely set, acute tubercles forming a trident (arrowed). Basal segment of chelicera with a ventral spur (Fig. 22D)

.... 2

Front edge of cephalothorax without a trident. Basal segment of chelicera without a ventral spur (except *Mitopus*) 8

2. Femur of pedipalp with conspicuous tubercles (sometimes spine-tipped) ventrally (arrowed)

.... 3

Femur of pedipalp without conspicuous tubercles ventrally 5

3. Patella of pedipalp with an apophysis (inside) (arrowed). Body length normally between 3.0 and 4.5 mm

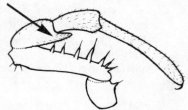

....*Lophopilio palpinalis* (p. 88)

Patella of pedipalp without an apophysis. Body length normally between 4.0 and 11.0 mm **4**

4. Femora of legs sharply angular in cross-section and edged with rows of acute denticles (Fig. 19D). Saddle conspicuous in male (arrowed) but less well defined in female. Body length up to about 5.5 mm

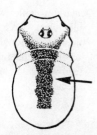

....*Lacinius ephippiatus* (p. 70)

Femora not angular or denticulate. Saddle (arrowed) not so greatly contrasted against background in either sex. Body length between 7.0 and 11.0 mm, the largest British species

.... *Odiellus spinosus* (p. 72)

5. Abdomen with conspicuous rows of tubercles (arrowed). Trident members rather slender and pointed, the central one about twice as long as the laterals (Figs. 18A & B)

.... *Paroligolophus meadii* (p. 68)

Rows of tubercles on abdomen, if present, not conspicuous. Trident members relatively short and stout **6**

6. Genital operculum clearly notched in female (arrowed); usually only indicated by a slightly darkened small indentation in male (arrowed). Ocularium silvery between eyes

....*Paroligolophus agrestis* (p. 66)

Genital operculum without a notch or sign of indentation 7

7. Ocularium with two rows of two to four tubercles; dark between eyes. Trident members strongly inclined upwards with accessory tubercles to the sides and rear (arrowed). A generally dark coloured species

....*Oligolophus hanseni* (p. 64)

Ocularium with two rows of four to seven tubercles; pale between eyes. Accessory tubercles, if any, not conspicuous

....*Oligolophus tridens* (p. 62)

8. Pedipalp with an apophysis on both tibia and patella (arrowed)

.... 9

Pedipalp without any apophyses 10

9. Ocularium crown-like with two rows of
exceptionally prominent spines

....*Megabunus diadema* (p. 84)

Ocularium without exceptionally prominent spines......................
.... *Rilaena triangularis* (p. 86)

10. Supracheliceral lamella with a pair of tubercles (arrowed). Male has
prominent, horned chelicerae (arrowed)

....*Phalangium opilio* (p. 78)

Supracheliceral lamella without tubercles **11**

11. Leg tibiae five-sided and
angular in cross section
(see figure). Basal segment
of chelicera with a ventral
spur (arrowed)

.... *Mitopus morio* and *M. m.* var. *ericaeus* (p. 74 and p. 76)

Leg tibiae almost rounded in cross section. Basal segment of
chelicera without ventral spur **12**

12. Ocularium with two rows of three to four
tubercles (arrowed). Dorsum of abdomen
with central pale line or series of pale spots.
Body length about 3.5–5.5 mm

....*Opilio saxatilis* (p. 82)

62

Ocularium with two rows of five to seven
   tubercles (arrowed). Dorsum without
   central pale line or row of spots. Body
   length about 5.5–8.0 mm

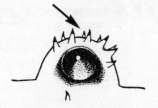

....*Opilio parietinus* (p. 80)

Oligolophus tridens (C. L. Koch)
(Fig. 15)

Opilio tridens C. L. Koch, 1836: *Die Arachniden* **3**: 14
Oligolophus tridens: Simon, 1879: *Les Arachnides de France* **7**: 251
Diagnosis: Trident and palpal claw present, the latter without pectination. Trident almost vertical. Saddle (Fig. 15A) characteristically dark and abruptly truncated. Needs careful comparison with *Lacinius ephippiatus* (p. 70). Penis distinct (see below and Figs. 15D, E).
Body length: male 3.5–4.5 mm, female 4.0–5.5 mm
Length of second leg: 15.0–20.0 mm
Body (Fig. 15A) yellow brown with variegated spots and usually with a dark saddle truncated on tergite 5. Female saddle noticeably straight-sided. Male abdomen somewhat pointed posteriorly. Ocularium relatively prominent in male, about as long as wide and slightly more than its length distant from front edge of the cephalothorax. Ocularium provided with four to seven modest, hair-tipped tubercles. Trident variable but usually almost vertical; its members tend to be equal in male (Fig. 15B, arrowed) but in female (Fig. 15C, arrowed) laterals tend to be shorter. Openings of odoriferous glands conspicuous. Meso- and metapeltidium and most abdominal tergites with a transverse row of hair-tipped tubercles.
Chelicerae shaped normally and with markings as in Fig. 15A; basal segment with well-developed ventral spur.
Pedipalps (Fig. 15B) yellow brown with darker patches, each segment furnished with hairs and short spines. Ventral surface of trochanter and femur with short, spine-tipped tubercles. Male tarsus with an inner-ventral series of micro-denticles as in Fig. 5E.
Legs coloured as pedipalps; femora, patellae and tibiae angular in cross-section and furnished with longitudinal rows of short black spines.
Penis (Figs. 15D, E): corpus long and slender throughout.
Occurrence. This species is common and widely distributed throughout the British Isles. It appears to have a preference for the ground layer of woods but it may also occur in the rank vegetation of marshes, hedgerows and gardens. It is commonly caught in pitfall traps but *O. tridens* also has the habit of ascending tree trunks and walls. It can be beaten from bushes and the low branches of trees, both angiosperms and conifers. Adults are present from about the end of July until the frosts;

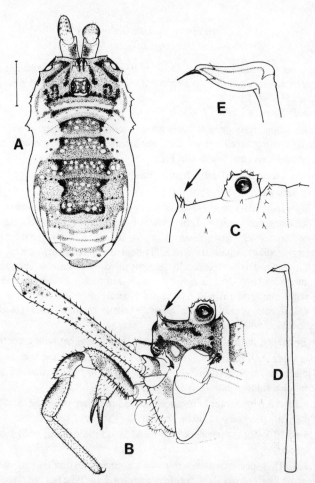

Fig. 15. *Oligolophus tridens*. A. Dorsal view of male body (bar = 1 mm); B. Lateral view of male cephalothorax (trident arrowed) with pedipalp and femur of leg 1; C. Lateral view of female cephalothorax dorsum showing trident (arrowed) and tubercles on ocularium; D. Lateral view of penis; E. Lateral view of glans penis.

individuals may survive in a sheltered place until about January. Eggs are laid in late summer and autumn; they hatch during the following April to July. Some individuals may remain immature until September, even in the south of England.

Type locality. Regensburg, East Germany. The first British record was by the Rev. O. Pickard-Cambridge (1890) from Bloxworth, Dorset and other places. (Map 8, p. 105) Abroad the species is distributed from France eastwards to Poland and Romania and northwards to 68°N including Finland and Iceland. In the Alps it occurs up to 1700 m. It has been introduced into eastern North America (Martens, 1978).

Oligolophus hanseni (Kraepelin)
(Fig. 16)

Acantholopus hansenii Kraepelin, 1896: *Mitt. naturh. Mus. Hamb*. **13**: 232
Oligolophus hansenii: O. Pickard-Cambridge, 1897: *Proc. Dorset nat. Hist. antiq. Fld. Club* **18**: 108
O. hanseni: Martens, 1978: *Tierwelt Dtl*. **64**: 313

Diagnosis: Palpal claw present but without pectination. Trident present but not prominent. Distinguished by its dark appearance and conspicuous ocularium. Penis unmistakable (see below and Figs. 16D, E).

Body length: male 3.3–4.0 mm, female 3.8–5.0 mm

Length of second leg: 15.0–18.0 mm

Body (Fig. 16A) dark greyish brown on dorsum with an indistinct saddle. Ocularium black and white with two rows of blunt, hair-tipped tubercles on top. Ocularium somewhat wider than long, its distance from front margin of cephalothorax about equals its width. Trident not prominent, central member usually longest and trident generally accompanied by a variable number of accessory tubercles (Fig. 16B, arrowed). Meso- and metapeltidium and abdominal tergites with transverse rows of hair-tipped tubercles forming white spots. Openings of odoriferous glands inconspicuous. Ventrum relatively pale coloured and may be speckled with white spots.

Chelicerae shaped normally, paler than body, basal segment with a ventral spur.

Pedipalps (Fig. 16C) paler than body, patella with an indistinct apophysis on inner side. Tibia relatively short and thick; male tarsus has a longitudinal series of micro-denticles (inner-ventral) as in Fig. 5E.

Legs pale brown with darker annulations, armature rather weak. Femora more or less cylindrical, patellae and tibiae angular.

Penis (Figs. 16D, E): corpus dark brown and broad throughout, unlike any other British species.

Occurrence. This species has something of a northerly distribution and while it is found in most kinds of woods, its preference is for Scots pine but not those in close plantations. It is nowhere abundant. Mature specimens may be beaten from the branches of trees and bushes mostly between August and November; it matures rather late and seems not to be long lived though it has been recorded in December (January in Holland, Spoek, 1963). Eggs laid the previous year hatch about June (May has been recorded) and immatures are present, in the ground and field layers, until September.

Type locality. Hamburg area. The first British record (Pickard-Cambridge, 1897) was from the neighbourhood of Edinburgh in 1896, collected by Mr. W. Evans. (Map 9, p. 105) Abroad the species occurs in the Pyrenees and Cantabrian Mts (to 1900 m) and from Belgium to Scandinavia and Poland (Martens, 1978).

Remarks. Female specimens found on oaks at Hurstbourne Park, Hants, in November 1985, had an unusually pale colouration with reddish brown and silvery patches on the dorsum.

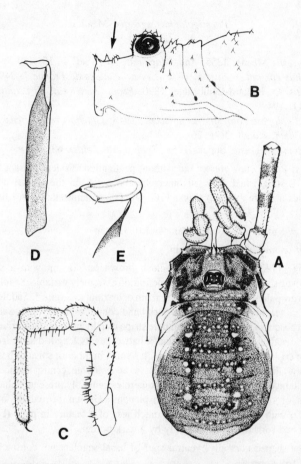

Fig. 16. *Oligolophus hanseni*. A. Dorsal view of male body with pedipalps and femur of leg 1 (bar = 1 mm); B. Lateral view of male cephalothorax showing form of tubercles on ocularium. Arrow points to accessory tubercles of trident; C. Outside lateral view of male left pedipalp; D. Lateral, partly dorsal, view of penis; E. Lateral view of glans penis.

Paroligolophus agrestis (Meade)
(Fig. 17)

Opilio agrestis Meade, 1855: *Ann. Mag. nat. Hist.* Ser. 2, **15**: 410
Oligolophus ephippiger Simon, 1879: *Les Arachnides de France* **7**: 249
O. agrestis: O. Pickard-Cambridge, 1890: *Proc. Dorset nat. Hist. antiq. Fld Club* **11**: 194
O. (Paroligolophus) agrestis: Lohmander, 1945: *Goteborgs K. Vetensk. -o. vitterhSamh. Handl.* **3**(9): 26
Paroligolophus agrestis Spoek, 1963: *Zool. Verh. Leiden* **63**: 58

Diagnosis: Palpal claw present but without pectination. Trident present but often obscure. Distinguished from all others by the notch on the genital operculum (sometimes obscure in male) (Figs. 17C, D). Penis unmistakable (see below and Fig. 17E).

Body length: male 3.0–4.0 mm, female 4.0–5.0 mm

Length of second leg: 14.0–18.0 mm

Body (Fig. 17A) silvery grey to pinkish brown on dorsum with a saddle of characteristic shape though pattern and definition extremely variable. Saddle usually has a narrow pale stripe down its centre from ocularium to tergite 5. Saddle broadly truncated at tergite 5 but a narrower dark band continues to tergite 7. Saddle may be almost absent in female but central pale stripe usually present. Ocularium silvery white, wider than long, about one and a half times its length distant from front margin of cephalothorax and provided with a small number of spicules best seen in lateral view (Fig. 17B). Trident inconspicuous and variable; central member usually largest and inclined forward. Accessory tubercles generally present behind trident. Openings of odoriferous glands inconspicuous. Genital operculum of female (Fig. 17D) with a deep notch. Notch much less of a feature in male (Fig. 17C, arrowed) and sometimes marked only by a dark border.

Chelicerae shaped normally, ventral spur of basal segment not conspicuous.

Pedipalps (Fig. 17B) pale brown, furnished with hairs and short spines longest on ventral surface of femur. Male tarsus has a longitudinal series of micro-denticles (inner-ventral) as in Fig. 5E.

Legs coloured as pedipalps but dark annulations occur on tibiae, patellae and distal parts of femora. Femora more or less cylindrical, tibiae markedly angular.

Penis (Fig. 17E): unmistakable, corpus long and very slender but with broad base; glans small, shorter than stylus.

Occurrence. This harvestman is widespread and it is probably the most abundant species in the British Isles. It may be found in woodland, parkland, grassland, sand-dunes, heaths, hedgerows and gardens. In woodland it inhabits every vegetational zone from the ground layer to the canopy of trees. In summer and autumn it can be beaten in large numbers from the branches of trees especially oak and Scots pine. However, *P. agrestis* may be absent on open heaths and in bogs. Individuals become mature from about the beginning of July and remain active

67

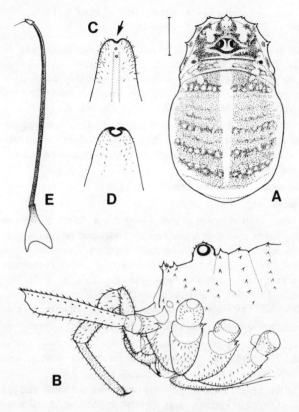

Fig. 17. *Paroligolophus agrestis*. A. Dorsal view of female body (bar = 1 mm); B. Lateral view of male cephalothorax with pedipalp and femur of leg 1; C. Male genital operculum showing notch (arrowed); D. Female genital operculum showing opening; E. Lateral view of penis.

until about December occasionally even surviving, in sheltered places, until February. Eggs are laid in late summer and autumn and hatch from late April onwards. Immatures may be found until September.

The species was first described by Meade (1855) from the British Isles. The author gave no particular locality but described *agrestis* as 'very common'. (Map 10, p. 106) Abroad the species is widely distributed in Europe from northern Iberia (to 1300 m in Cantabrian Mts) to southern Scandinavia and Poland but it is not recorded from Hungary and Czechoslovakia (Martens, 1978). It has been introduced into British Columbia and Washington State (Bragg & Holmberg, 1974).

68

Paroligolophus meadii (O. P.-Cambridge)
(Fig. 18)

Oligolophus meadii O. Pickard-Cambridge, 1890: *Proc. Dorset nat. Hist.
antiq. Fld. Club* **11**: 198
Odius meadii: Roewer, 1912: *Abh. naturw. Ver. Hamburg* **20**(1): 65
Odiellus meadii: Roewer, 1923: *Die Weberknechte der Erde*: 729
Paroligolophus meadii: Martens, 1978: *Tiewelt Dtl.* **64**: 320

Diagnosis: Palpal claw present but without pectination. Trident forward pointing
with central member prominent (Fig. 18A). Distinguished from all others by its
transverse rows of acute tubercles on dorsum (Fig. 18B). Penis distinct (see below
and Figs. 18C, D).

Body length: male 2.3–3.0 mm, female 2.8–3.8 mm

Length of second leg: 10.0–15.0 mm

Body (Fig. 18B) straw coloured or with a greyish hue. Saddle marked by regular
dark brown patches enclosing a pale centre. Abdominal tergites with transverse
rows of stout, acute, often whitish tubercles. Ocularium wider than long and about
one and a half times its length distant from front margin of cephalothorax. Lateral
margin of cephalothorax with four prominent tubercles (Fig. 18B). Trident conspicuous, central member (Fig. 18A, arrowed) much longer than laterals and inclined at about 50°. Openings of odoriferous glands inconspicuous. Ventrum pale.

Chelicerae shaped normally, pale coloured, basal segment without ventral spur.

Pedipalps (Fig. 18A) pale coloured, sometimes with lateral brown spots on femur
and patella. Trochanter and femur with a number of ventral, spine-tipped
tubercles, particularly in male.

Legs pale yellow brown darkening distally on femora and tibiae and armed with
rows of short spines. Femora more or less cylindrical, patellae and tibiae
somewhat angular in cross section.

Penis (Figs. 18C, D): stylus curved and slightly longer than glans; a pair of setae
occur unusually close to apex of glans (Fig. 18D).

Occurrence. This species is by no means common though fairly widely distributed
in England and Wales. It occurs in the ground layer of relatively dry habitats such
as chalk downs, heaths and sand dunes. Sites with a combination of grass and
heather appear to be preferred. It may also be found under old turves and stones
and often in association with *Opilio saxatilis*. Adults are present from July to
December during which period the eggs are laid. Eggs hatch the following spring;
immatures have not been recorded before late May.

Type locality. Bloxworth, Dorset from where it was described by Pickard-
Cambridge in 1890. (Map 11, p. 106) For a long time it appeared that *meadii* might
be a British endemic though it was known from Guernsey (1955) and this suggested
that it would be found on the Continent of Europe. Indeed, Martens has recently
(1978) recorded the species from the Cantabrian Mountains in northern Spain.

69

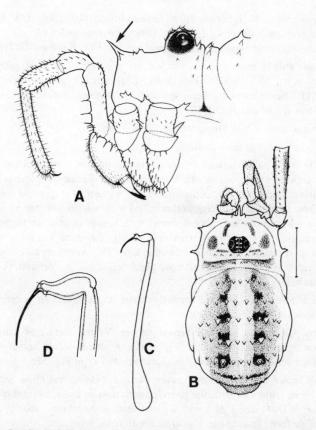

Fig. 18. *Paroligolophus meadii*. A. Lateral view of male cephalothorax (with pedipalp) showing elongate central trident member (arrowed). B. Dorsal view of male body with pedipalps and femur of leg 1 (bar = 1 mm); C. Lateral view of penis; D. Lateral view of glans penis.

70

Lacinius ephippiatus (C. L. Koch)
(Fig. 19)

Opilio ephippiatus C. L. Koch, 1835: *Faunae Insect. Germ. init.* **128**: 17
Acantholopus ephippiatus: C. L. Koch, 1848: *Die Arachniden* **15**: 121
Lacinius ephippiatus: Roewer, 1912: *Abh. naturw. Ver. Hamburg* **20**(1): 78

Diagnosis: Palpal claw present but without pectination. Trident prominent, members equal and slender (Fig. 19B). Legs angular and strongly armed (Fig. 19D). Needs careful comparison with *Oligolophus tridens* (p. 62). Penis distinct (see below and Fig. 19E).

Body length: male 3.5–4.5 mm, female 4.5–5.5 mm

Length of second leg: 16.0–20.0 mm

Body (Fig. 19A) pale yellowish brown or grey on dorsum with a blackish brown rectangular saddle truncated on fifth abdominal tergite. Saddle conspicuous in male but often indistinct in female. Ocularium slightly wider than long, about one length distant from front margin of cephalothorax and with two rows of four to six short but acute tubercles on top. Cephalothorax with a number of acute tubercles on lateral margin. Trident conspicuous (Fig. 19B), the three members slender, approximately equal in length and inclined at about 75°. Accessory tubercles occur behind trident. Openings of odoriferous glands conspicuous. Ventrum pale with white patches.

Chelicerae pale yellow, shaped normally; basal segment with an inconspicuous ventral spur.

Pedipalps pale yellow with dark brown patches. Ventral surface of femur with numerous spine-tipped tubercles (Fig. 19C, arrowed). Male tarsus with a longitudinal series of micro-denticles (inner-ventral) as in Fig. 5E.

Legs pale brown with darker annulations. Femora, patellae and tibiae angular in cross section; femora in particular provided with rows of acute, inclined tubercles as in Fig. 19D. Coxae 1 & 2 with a prominent, acute tubercle apically on the posterior surface. Trochanters also armed with acute tubercles.

Penis (Fig. 19E): corpus narrows above mid-point in dorsal or ventral view; stylus relatively short and stout.

Occurrence. This species is widely distributed in the British Isles but rarely abundant. It lives in the ground layer of deciduous woods, marshes and meadows; at night it may move into the herb layer. *L. ephippiatus* matures relatively early in the year; in a good season some individuals may mature as early as May. It appears not to survive beyond September; the eggs overwinter and hatch somewhat earlier than most species, normally in April.

Type locality. Austria. The first British record was by Meade (1855) who wrote 'It is found abundantly in various parts of England and Wales'. (Map 12, p. 106) Abroad the species is distributed through most of Europe from the Pyrenees to Bulgaria and Poland and to 62°N in Scandinavia. It occurs up to 1650 m in the Alps (Martens, 1978).

71

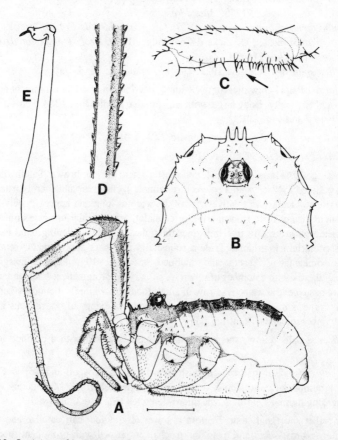

Fig. 19. *Lacinius ephippiatus*. A. Lateral view of male body with pedipalp and leg 1 (bar = 1 mm); B. Dorsal view of male cephalothorax showing three equal members of trident; C. Outside lateral view of male pedipalp femur showing spine-tipped tubercles (arrowed); D. Section of femur of leg 2 showing angular edges furnished with acute tubercles; E. Lateral view of penis.

Odiellus spinosus (Bosc)
(Fig. 20)

Phalangium spinosum Bosc, 1792: *Bull. Sci. Soc. Philom. Corresp.* **1**: 18
Opilio histrix: Meade, 1855: *Ann. Mag. nat. Hist.* Ser. 2, **15**: 407
Acantholophus spinosus: Simon, 1879: *Les Arachnides de France* **7**: 261
Oligolophus spinosus: O. Pickard-Cambridge, 1890: *Proc. Dorset nat. Hist.*
   antiq. Fld. Club **11**: 201
Odiellus spinosus: Roewer, 1923: *Die Weberknechte der Erde*: 725

Diagnosis: Palpal claw present but without pectination. Trident prominent and set almost horizontally. Body large, with a distinctive saddle (Fig. 20A). Penis distinct (see below and Fig. 20E).

Body length: male 6.5–8.5 mm, female 7.0–11.0 mm

Length of second leg: 20.0–28.0 mm

Body (Fig. 20A) large and broad, yellowish grey to greyish brown. Saddle distinctive, outlined in black with a pale centre, almost rectangular and sharply truncated posteriorly. Ocularium relatively small, as wide as long and approximately twice its length distant from front margin of cephalothorax. Ocularium pale on top and furnished with three to five indistinct tubercles. A pale, widening band extends from ocularium to trident. Trident robust, its members approximately equal in size, somewhat divergent and inclined at about 10°. Lateral margin of cephalothorax with a number of tubercles of varying prominence. Each abdominal tergite has a central transverse row of small tubercles while the boundary between each tergite is marked by a row of brown spots. Openings of odoriferous glands rather inconspicuous. Ventrum pale.

Chelicerae pale yellow, shaped normally, basal segment with a distinct ventral spur.

Pedipalps (Fig. 20B) pale or yellowish brown with darker spots and stripes. Femur with a number of conspicuous ventral spine-tipped tubercles. Male tarsus with a dense longitudinal field of black micro-denticles (Fig. 20C, arrowed).

Legs rather short and stout. Femora more or less cylindrical, patellae and tibiae angular in cross section. Coxae and trochanters armed with prominent tubercles but generally legs have only hairs in longitudinal rows.

Penis (Fig. 20E): corpus with dorsal apical concave plate.

Occurrence. This species occurs in England south east of a line from the Severn to the Humber. Here it appears to have a preference for warm, sheltered man-made habitats and can be numerous in gardens, parks, around buildings and on derelict sites. Adults may be found under window ledges and similar places, sometimes almost sitting on top of one another when resting during the day.

Usually it lives on the ground but will ascend bushes and trees as well as walls. Pitfall-trapping is likely to be effective. The young, which live among grass and debris, emerge from over-wintering eggs in June and mature around August; individuals may survive until the end of the year.

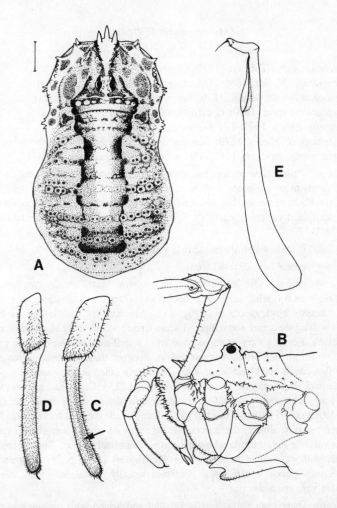

Fig. 20. *Odiellus spinosus.* A. Dorsal view of female body (bar = 1 mm); B. Lateral view of male cephalothorax with pedipalp and femur plus patella of leg 1; C. Inside lateral view of right male pedipalp tibia and tarsus showing series of denticulae on tarsus (arrowed); D. Inside lateral view of right female pedipalp tibia and tarsus; E. Lateral view of penis.

Type locality. Paris. The species was included in the British list by Meade (1855, sub *Opilio histrix*) though he had not actually seen an English specimen. (Map 13, p. 106) Abroad the species is found in western Europe from northern Iberia to Holland (local in Germany) and across northern Italy into part of Yugoslavia; it avoids high ground. The records from Sardinia and North Africa require confirmation (Martens, 1978).

74

Mitopus morio (Fabricius)
(Fig. 21)

Phalangium morio Fabricius, 1799: *Reise nach Norwegen*: 341
P. urnigerum: Meade, 1855: *Ann. Mag. nat. Hist.* Ser. 2, **15**: 401
Oligolophus morio: Simon, 1879: *Les Arachnides de France* 7: 241
O. palliatus: Simon, 1879: *Les Arachnides de France* 7: 243
O. alpinus: Simon 1879: *Les Arachnides de France* 7: 244
O. cinerascens: Simon, 1879: *Les Arachnides de France* 7: 246
Mitopus morio: Roewer, 1912: *Abh. naturw. Ver. Hamburg* **20**(1): 45

Diagnosis: Palpal claw present but without pectination. Trident virtually absent. Basal segment of chelicera with ventral spur as in Fig. 22D. Supra-cheliceral lamella without tubercles. Leg tibiae angular in cross section. Much more common than the upland variety *ericaeus* (p. 76). Compare penis carefully (see below and Figs. 21D, E).

Body length: male 4.0–6.0 mm, female 6.0–8.5 mm

Length of second leg: 20.0–40.0 mm

Body extremely variable in colouration and pattern. Males usually pale brown or grey on dorsum with transverse spots and often with a strongly marked, predominantly black saddle as in Fig. 21A. Alternatively, saddle may be black-edged with a pale centre and a median white stripe; occasionally almost entire dorsum black. Females vary in appearance from a well-marked black saddle pattern to a uniform greyish brown without saddle. Between these extremes, female saddles often edged black and white with a relatively pale centre, sometimes with a longitudinal stripe, similar to var. *ericaeus* (Fig. 22A). Ocularium silvery, wider than long, one and one half times its length distant from front margin of cephalothorax and with two rows of small, hair-tipped tubercles on top (Fig. 21C). Trident virtually absent; the number of tubercles on dorsal surface of cephalothorax variable as is their development across abdominal tergites. Supra-cheliceral lamella without median tubercles (see *Phalangium opilio* p. 78). Openings of odoriferous glands conspicuous. Ventrum usually more pale than dorsum, compare var. *ericaeus*.

Chelicerae shaped normally, relatively stout and armed with denticles in male. Ventral spur on basal segment well developed (as in Fig. 22D, arrowed).

Pedipalps (Fig. 21B) variable in colouration; femur, patella and tibia often with blackish brown pattern (Fig. 21A). Small hair-tipped tubercles occur on trochanter and femur; tarsus of male with an inner-ventral series of micro-denticles as in Fig. 5E.

Legs yellowish brown but, especially in male, marked on femur and tibia with blackish brown. Femora 1 & 2 more or less cylindrical; femora 3 & 4 and all tibiae angular in cross section. Femora usually with rows of acute black denticles, each preceeded by a short spine.

Penis (Fig. 21D): glans with a retractable bladder and ventral apophysis; similar to var. *ericaeus* but corpus relatively short and stout.

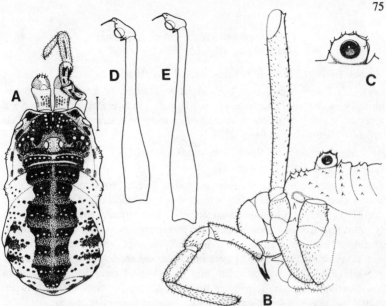

Fig. 21. *Mitopus morio*. A. Dorsal view of male body (bar = 1 mm); B. Lateral view of male cephalothorax with pedipalp and femur of leg 1; C. Lateral view of male ocularium showing form of tubercles; D. Lateral view of penis. *M. m.* var. *ericaeus*; E. Lateral view of penis. [Both penes drawn to scale.]

Occurrence. This species is widely distributed throughout the British Isles and it has a broad ecological tolerance. It is common in both lowlands and uplands inhabiting woodlands, heathlands, grasslands, moorlands and hedgerows. It is abundant and conspicuous on upland grasslands; in woodland it occupies all vegetational zones. In the lowlands adults are present from the beginning of July until the frosts. Eggs laid during the period of maturity hatch in April or May, juveniles may be found until the end of August.

Type locality. Norway. The first British record (sub *Phalangium urnigerum*) was by Meade (1855) who described it as generally distributed over England. (Map 14, p. 107) Abroad the species is exceptionally wide in its distribution throughout much of the Nearctic and Palaearctic from North Africa to Spitzbergen. It occurs up to the snow line, c. 3000 m, in the Pyrenees and Alps (Martens, 1978).

Remarks. M. morio is a highly variable species. Some early authors described the various forms as separate species while others, more realistically, considered them to be subspecies or varieties of *M. morio*, e.g. *M. morio alpinus* (Herbst) and *M. morio cinerascens* (C. L. Koch). However, since Roewer (1912, 1923) most have considered these and other varieties to be nothing more than synonyms of *M. morio*. They have been unable to assign any of the morphological character states regarding limb length, armature, colouration etc. to discrete groups as intermediates invariably occur. The reader is referred to Jennings (1983) and Martens (1988).

76

Mitopus morio variety *ericaeus* Jennings
(Figs. 21, 22)

Mitopus ericaeus Jennings, 1982: *J. Zool. Lond.* **198**(1): 2

Diagnosis: Palpal claw present but without pectination. Trident virtually absent. Much less widespread than *M. morio* (p. 61); differs in its ecology, colouration and generally stronger armature, male ocularium more prominent. Penis proportions indicative (see below and Fig. 21E).

Body length: male 3.5–5.0 mm, female 6.0–8.0 mm

Length of second leg: 23.0–35.0 mm

Body (Fig. 22A) similar to *M. morio* but colour usually brown, often tinged pink, heavily mottled and with a strikingly marked saddle. Saddle edged black and white usually enclosing a pale longitudinal stripe. Trident virtually absent and replaced by tubercles variable in their number and prominence. Armature somewhat more developed than in typical *M. morio* especially in male where dorsum furnished with many acute, black-tipped tubercles. Ocularium noticeably large and upright in male (Fig. 22C) and provided with two rows of three to five prominent tubercles. Ventrum usually marbled brown with grey patches; contrast between ventral and dorsal colouration less in var. *ericaeus* than in *M. morio*.

Chelicerae shaped normally, strongly patterned and relatively robust in male (Fig. 22D) with numbers of dorsal denticles. Ventral spur on basal segment well developed (arrowed).

Pedipalps (Fig. 22B) with dark patches, spines and denticles; femur with medial-apical tuft of setae. Male tarsus has a longitudinal field of micro-denticles (inner-ventral, as in Fig. 5E).

Legs strongly armed with longitudinal rows of acute black tubercles interspersed with short spines; most segments angular in cross section.

Penis (Fig. 21E): corpus relatively long and slender compared with *M. morio*. Note bladder and apophysis at base of glans.

Occurrence. This variety has been identified from upland areas of northern England and Scotland (Map 15, p. 107). It appears to be restricted to moorland habitats above 250 metres where, typically, heather or ling (*Calluna vulgaris*) is dominant and with co-dominants such as *Pteridium aquilinum*, *Vaccinium myrtilis* and *Eriophorum vaginatum*. It ranges over the field layer and may be collected by hand, sweeping and pitfall-trapping. Invariably it is in co-existence with *M. morio*. On the basis of regular pitfall trapping, Jennings (1982) found that specimens of var. *ericaeus* were always in a later instar than those of *M. morio*. The median date for var. *ericaeus* becoming adult was nineteen days earlier than *M. morio*. However, *M. morio* adults had a greater temporal spread, occurring in traps over a period of twelve weeks compared with three weeks for var. *ericaeus* (July/August). It is possible that the life cycle of var. *ericaeus* takes longer than one year.

Type locality. Muggleswick Common, Co. Durham, England. Abroad *ericaeus* has been reported from the Pyrenees (Martens, 1988).

77

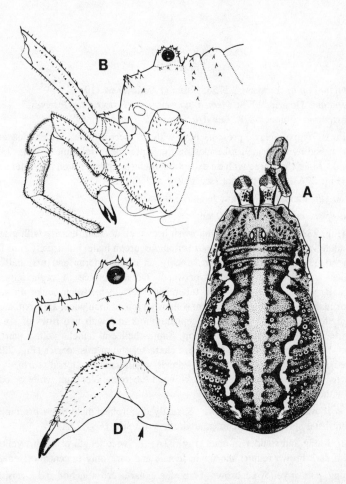

Fig. 22. *Mitopus m.* var. *ericaeus*. A. Dorsal view of female body (bar = 1 mm); B. Lateral view of female cephalothorax with pedipalp and femur of leg 1; C. Lateral view of male cephalothorax dorsum showing form of tubercles on ocularium; D. Outside lateral view of left male chelicera showing ventral spur (arrowed) on basal segment. [For penis see Fig. 21 E.]

Remarks. It is felt that *ericaeus* does not justify the status of a species as originally described. On purely morphological criteria an unequivocal identification may prove to be impossible; we have found intermediates for most character states. Its separation from *morio* has been claimed also on the basis of phenological data (Jennings, 1982, 1983) but data which would convince us of the isolation of the two as quite separate species have yet to be found.

Phalangium opilio Linnaeus
(Figs. 23)

Phalangium opilio Linnaeus, 1758: *Systema Naturae* ed. **10**: 619
P. cornutum: Degeer, 1778: *Mém. pour servir à l'histoire des Insectes* **7**: 173
P. brevicorne: Simon, 1879: *Les Arachnides de France* **7**: 198

Diagnosis: Palpal claw present but without pectination. Trident absent. Distinguished by two small tubercles on the supra-cheliceral lamella (Fig. 23B, arrowed). Male chelicerae with an exceptionally large apophysis on the distal segment (Fig. 23A). Penis distinct (see below and Fig. 23C).

Body length: male 4.0–7.0 mm, female 5.0–9.0 mm

Length of second leg: 30.0–48.0 mm

Body (Fig. 23A) whitish grey or yellowish brown on dorsum, usually with a saddle. Saddle variable in depth of colour (often obscure in male) but usually runs the length of the dorsum. It is shaped broadly on cephalothorax and first half of abdomen while strongly indented between. Dorsal surface of cephalothorax (Fig. 23B) with many black-tipped tubercles especially between ocularium and anterior margin; no trident. Ocularium somewhat longer than wide, approximately one length from anterior margin of cephalothorax and with two rows of six to ten acute, black-tipped tubercles on top. Supra-cheliceral lamella with a pair of median, black-tipped tubercles which are characteristic of this species (Fig. 23B, arrowed). Openings of odoriferous glands conspicuous. Dorsal surface of abdomen with transverse rows of black-tipped tubercles. Ventrum white or pale grey, without spots.

Chelicerae robust, yellowish brown. Sexually dimorphic: male has a prominent horn on distal segment, sometimes attaining great size (Fig. 23A).

Pedipalps long and slender in male (Fig. 23A) (*c.* twice length of body), yellow but with dark brown femur; shorter in female and dark only in centre of femur.

Legs long, pale or yellowish brown. Femora angular in cross section and furnished with five longitudinal rows of acute, black-tipped tubercles.

Penis (Fig. 23C) narrows abruptly in upper part of corpus (lateral view).

Occurrence. A common and widely distributed species frequenting open woodland, hedgerows, grassland, derelict land and gardens. It occurs on tree trunks and walls (usually the shady side) and is often found in rank vegetation such as nettle beds. *P. opilio* is scarce on open moorland and heaths but frequent in coastal regions. It may be collected by all methods and sometimes comes to the entomologists' sugar patches. Individuals become adult from June onwards and may survive until December. Eggs are laid usually in autumn and hatch the following spring; juveniles occur mostly from May to August; they remain in the ground layer. On the south coast an early generation (adult in May) has been observed with the probability that a second generation occurs later in the year.

Type locality (Linnaeus, 1758) 'Europa, Amerika'. The first British record is

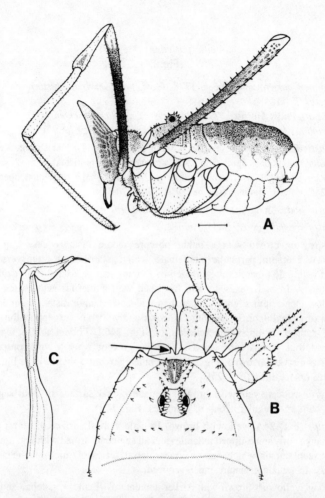

Fig. 23. *Phalangium opilio*. A. Lateral view of male body with chelicera, pedipalp and femur of leg 1 (bar = 1 mm); B. Dorsal view of female cephalothorax showing supra-cheliceral lamella (arrowed); C. Distal portion of penis (lateral view).

obscure. (Map 16, p. 107) Abroad the species ranges throughout Europe as far as southern Sweden and up to 2400 m in the Italian Apennines (Martens, 1978); it also occurs in Asia and North America and has been introduced into New Zealand.

80

Opilio parietinus (Degeer)
(Fig. 24)

Phalangium parietinum Degeer, 1778: *Mém. pour servir à l'histoire des Insectes* **7**: 116
Opilio parietinus: Herbst, 1799: *Natursyst. Ungeflüg. Insekten* **3**: 12
O. parietinus (part): Roewer, 1923: *Weberknechte der Erde*: 770

Diagnosis: Palpal claw present but without pectination. Trident absent. Ventrum with conspicuous dark spots (Fig. 24A, arrowed). Distinguished from *O. saxatilis* (p. 82) by its larger size, ocularium (Fig. 24C) and shape of genital operculum (Fig. 24D). Penis distinct (see below and Fig. 24E).

Length of body: male 5.0–7.0 mm, female 6.0–9.0 mm

Length of second leg: 35.0–55.0 mm

Body grey or brown with a rather obscure saddle (usually absent in male, Fig. 24A). Dorsum, particularly in female, with a pattern of dark transverse bars, spotted with pale tubercles and crossed by longitudinal pale band from ocularium to posterior. In both sexes dorsum furnished with numerous acute black-tipped tubercles. Ocularium slightly longer than wide, one length distant from anterior margin of cephalothorax and with two rows of five or six (exceptionally four to eight), acute black-tipped tubercles on top (Fig. 24C). Trident absent. Openings of odoriferous glands conspicuous. Ventrum grey or whitish with conspicuous dark brown spots (arrowed, Fig. 24A). Genital operculum shaped as in Fig. 24D, compare *O. saxatilis* (Fig. 25D).

Chelicerae robust, yellowish brown. In male dorsal surface of both segments armed with an irregular group of denticles (Fig. 24B).

Pedipalps (Fig. 24A) yellowish brown. In male ventral surface of femur armed with many short, spine-tipped tubercles and all segments armed with scattered denticles except tarsus which has an inner-ventral series of micro-denticles as in Fig. 5E. In female armature much reduced.

Legs long, yellowish brown with darker annulations. Femora, patellae and tibiae furnished with rows of denticles and acute black-tipped tubercles. Femora in male angular in cross-section.

Penis (Fig. 24E) with two concave plates, rounded and without setae, on distal section of corpus at junction of glans.

Occurrence. Widespread in the British Isles and highly synanthropic; common on walls, fences, buildings and even found in the centre of London. Also found on tree trunks and bushes; the young tend to occur in rough grass, litter and under debris. Adults may be found from July to December, eggs are laid in the autumn and hatch in April or May.

Type locality. Sweden. The first British record is obscure. (Map 17, p. 107) The original range of the species is considered to be the Caucasus/ Asia Minor region, most likely in rocky habitats (Gruber & Hunt, 1973). With the assistance of human

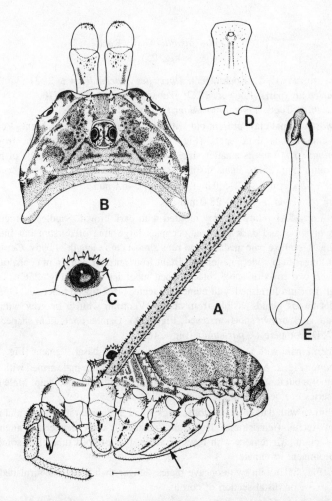

Fig. 24. *Opilio parietinus*. A. Lateral view of male body showing ventral spotting (arrowed) with pedipalp and femur of leg 1 (bar = 1 mm); B. Dorsal view of male cephalothorax with chelicerae; C. Lateral view of male ocularium showing form of tubercles; D. Genital operculum (male); E. Dorsal view of penis.

transport, the distribution now includes most of the western Palaearctic (to 63°N), the Nearctic and Tasmania. In the European Alps it occurs up to 1300 m (Martens, 1978).

Opilio saxatilis C. L. Koch
(Fig. 25)

Opilio saxatilis C. L. Koch, 1839: *Über. des Arachnidensyst.* **2**: 21
O. parietinus (part): Roewer, 1923: *Weberknechte der Erde*: 770
O. saxatilis: Todd, 1948: *Entomologist's mon. Mag.* **84**: 109
Diagnosis: Palpal claw present but without pectination. Trident absent. Ventrum with conspicuous dark spots (Fig. 25A, arrowed). Distinguished from *O. parietinus* (p. 80) by its smaller size, ocularium (Fig. 25C) and shape of genital operculum (Fig. 25D). Penis distinct (see below and Fig. 25E).
Length of body: male 3.2–5.0 mm, female 4.5–6.0 mm
Length of second leg: 18.0–28.0 mm
Body (Fig. 25A) yellowish-grey mottled with dark brown. Saddle, marked by a series of spots and dark patches, occupies large area of dorsum but intensity variable. Usually a pale median band runs almost entire length of body. Ocularium rather longer than wide, one length distant from anterior margin of cephalothorax and with two rows of acute, black-tipped tubercles on top (Fig. 25C). Trident absent. Dorsum furnished with numerous acute, black-tipped tubercles. Openings of odoriferous glands visible from above. Ventrum whitish or grey with conspicuous dark brown spots (arrowed, Fig. 25A). Genital operculum shaped as in Fig. 25D, compare *O. parietinus* (Fig. 24D).
Chelicerae pale with an oblong dark brown patch on basal segment (Fig. 25B).
Pedipalps (Fig. 25A) yellow mottled with brown. Femur in male armed with series of denticles but few on patella and none on tibia or on female pedipalp. Male tarsus with series of micro-denticles.
Legs brown with darker annulations. Legs 1 and 3 in male rather stout and round in cross-section (femur-tibia); legs 2 and 4 markedly more slender and angular in cross-section. All femora with rows of acute, black-tipped tubercles, somewhat less prominent in female.
Penis (Fig. 25E) with two concave plates, longer than wide and furnished with many hairs, on distal section of corpus.
Occurrence. A widespread species occurring in the ground and field layers of relatively dry habitats. It occurs in open woodlands, on heaths, grasslands (especially limestone) and in gardens. It is common in coastal regions particularly on sand dunes where it lives among marram and other plants with reasonable cover. *O. saxatilis* may be found under stones and also under debris in disturbed areas. Adults occur from July to December. Eggs are laid in the autumn and hatch the following spring.
Type locality. Regensburg, West Germany. The first British record was by the Rev. O. Pickard-Cambridge (1890) (Isle of Portland). (Map 18, p. 108).
Abroad the species is distributed across most of Central Europe from France to the Black Sea and Greece (where it occurs up to 2650 m, Martens, 1978), and on to Turkey. It has been introduced into Israel.

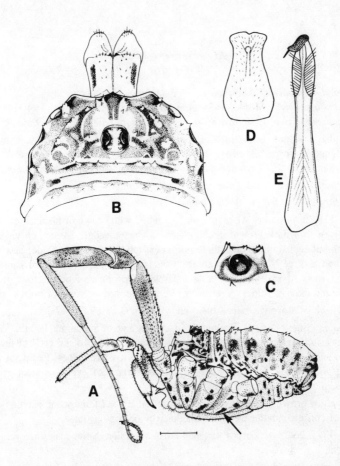

Fig. 25. *Opilio saxatilis*. A. Lateral view of male body showing ventral spotting (arrowed) with pedipalp and leg 1 (bar = 1 mm); B. Dorsal view of male cephalothorax with chelicerae; C. Lateral view of male ocularium showing form of tubercles; D. Genital operculum (male); E. Dorsal, partly lateral, view of penis.

Remarks. It is curious that this distinct species should ever have been considered to be the young of *O. parietinus* (Roewer, 1923). Indeed, Todd (1948), Sankey (1949a) and Spoek (1963) all report the species has never even been found together with *O. parietinus*.

84

Megabunus diadema (Fabricius)
(Fig. 26)

Phalangium diadema Fabricius, 1779: *Reise nach Norwegen*: 339
Megabunus insignis Meade, 1855: *Ann. Mag. nat. Hist.* Ser. 2, **15**: 406
M. diadema: Thorell, 1876: *Annali Mus. civ. Stor. nat. Giacomo Doria* **8**: 464

Diagnosis: Palpal claw present but without pectination. Trident absent. Distinguished from all others by its exceptionally prominent spines on the ocularium (Figs. 26A, B). Pedipalp with three apophyses (Fig. 26B). Males rare.

Body length: male 2.6–3.2 mm, female 3.2–4.8 mm

Length of second leg: 15.0–20.0 mm

Body (Fig. 26A) silvery white and partly mottled with brown or blackish patches. Usually with a dark brown, double-diamond shaped saddle. Abdomen virtually smooth but cephalothorax has three prominent tubercles on either side, best seen from above (Fig. 26B). Trident absent. Ocularium prominent and remarkable for its two rows of exceptionally long tubercles. Openings of odoriferous glands visible and dark in colour. Ventrum white with transverse rows of brown spots.

Chelicerae pale brown, rather small and of normal shape.

Pedipalps (Figs. 26A, B) yellowish in colour and of moderate length. Three apophyses occur on inner side positioned, respectively, at distal ends of femur, patella and tibia; each is furnished with short, bristle-like spines. Pedipalps also armed with spine-tipped tubercles on ventral surface of every segment except patella, most prominent on femur.

Legs yellow brown and relatively slender. Distal ends of femora and patellae with pairs of conspicuous tubercles. A smaller pair occurs on tibiae.

Penis (Figs. 26C, D): corpus flattened dorso-ventrally. Note: males are very infrequent.

Occurrence. A widespread species occurring in and above the ground layer of woodland, heathland and moorland. It appears to be commonest in the wetter and upland regions of Great Britain while it is most scarce in East Anglia. *Megabunus* has an appearance which enables it to blend with the lichen found on timber, rocks and heather. Adults have been noted in most months of the year but mostly from April onwards. Oviposition occurs in late summer with the eggs hatching the same year. It is possible that some individuals may survive into a third calendar year.

Type locality. Norway. The first British record (sub *insignis*) was by Meade (1855) who mentioned Bradford, North Wales and 'other parts of England'. (Map 19, p. 108) On the Continent of Europe the species is considered to be rather rare (Spoek, 1963). It is restricted to northern Spain, the coast of Normandy (France), part of the coast of Norway, the Faroe Islands and the south of Iceland. It occurs up to 2000 m in the Pyrenees (Martens, 1978).

Remarks. In all collections females far outnumber males; parthenogenetic reproduction has been proved to occur by Phillipson (1959) (see p. 14).

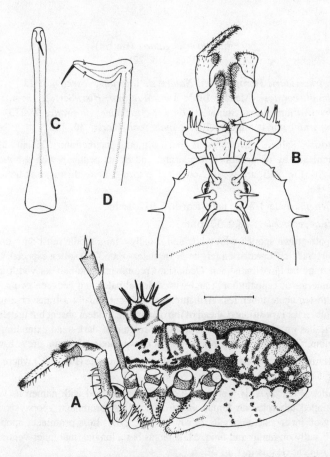

Fig. 26. *Megabunus diadema*. A. Lateral view of female body with pedipalp and femur plus patella of leg 1 (bar = 1 mm); B. Dorsal view of female cephalothorax and pedipalps; C. Ventral view of penis (after Martens, 1978); D. Lateral view of distal portion of penis (after Martens, 1978).

Rilaena triangularis (Herbst)
(Figs. 1 & 27)

Opilio triangularis Herbst, 1799: *Natursyst. Ungeflüg. Insekten* **3**: 12
Megabunus corniger: Meade, 1855: *Ann. Mag. nat. Hist.* Ser. 2, **15**: 405
Platybunus triangularis: Simon, 1879: *Les Arachnides de France* **7**: 223
Rilaena triangularis: Starega, 1973: *Annls zool. Warsz.* **30**: 143

Diagnosis: Palpal claw present but without pectination. Trident absent. Distinguished by its prominent ocularium and by its pedipalp with a noticeable apophysis (Fig. 27B, arrowed). Active in the spring. Penis distinct (see below and Fig. 27E).

Body length: male 3.7–4.5 mm, female 5.0–7.0 mm

Length of second leg: 28.0–38.0 mm

Body pale brown spotted with white and usually with a saddle most dark towards the rear. Saddle truncated on tergite 5. In males (Fig. 27A), often especially pale, saddle may be quite indistinct. Ocularium prominent, one-half its width distant from anterior of cephalothorax and with a dorsal pale band between two rows of seven to ten acute tubercles. Armature variable but usually a transverse row of small tubercles is positioned ahead of the ocularium. Trident absent but usually one tubercle lies on margin of cephalothorax in middle of dark band extending from ocularium. Openings of odoriferous glands conspicuous. Ventrum greyish-white.

Chelicerae pale brown and shaped normally except in male (Fig. 27C) where distal segment bears dorsal apophysis.

Pedipalps (Figs. 27A, B) yellowish-brown and furnished with numerous ventral spine-tipped tubercles on femur and trochanter. A prominent apophysis arises distally on inner side of patella (arrowed, Fig. 27B). Less prominent apophyses occur distally on femur and tibia. Male tarsus has a longitudinal inner-ventral row of micro-denticles as in Fig. 5E.

Legs pale yellow brown, femora with longitudinal rows of acute, inclined tubercles.

Penis (Fig. 27E): corpus, glans and stylus relatively long and slender; corpus strongly curved in lateral view.

Occurrence. This species is widespread and most often occurs in the ground and field layers of damp woodland. It may be taken in pitfall-traps and is sometimes beaten from bushes and the lower branches of trees. Adults tend to occur higher in the vegetational strata than juveniles. The season of maturity is unusually early: April to July. Eggs are laid in early summer; hatching occurs later in the summer and also during the autumn. Juveniles can be found from August to May and the winter is passed in about the third or fourth instar at which stage the ocularium is very conspicuous.

Type locality. Berlin. The first British record (sub *Megabunus corniger* (Hermann)) was by Meade (1855) who found it in 'different parts of England'.

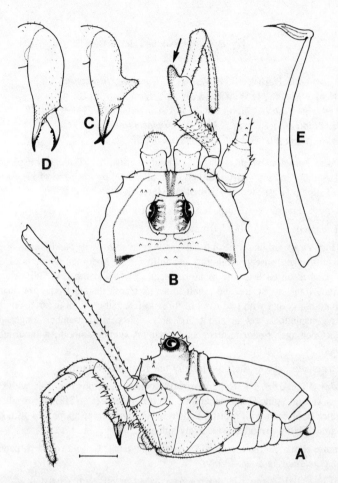

Fig. 27. *Rilaena triangularis*. A. Lateral view of male body with pedipalp and femur of leg 1 (bar = 1 mm); B. Dorsal view of male cephalothorax with right pedipalp (apophysis on patella arrowed); C. Inside lateral view of left male chelicera showing apophysis on distal segment; D. Similar view of female chelicera; E. Lateral view of penis.

(Map 20, p. 108). Abroad the species occurs widely in Europe (absent Iberia) as far east as western Russia. It extends northwards to 68°N (Finland) and occurs up to 2200 m in the southern Alps (Martens, 1978). It has been introduced into British Columbia and Washington State (Bragg & Holmberg, 1974).

Lophopilio palpinalis (Herbst)
(Fig. 28)

Opilio palpinalis Herbst, 1799: *Natursyst. Ungeflüg. Insekten* **3**: 16
O. terricola: Meade, 1855: *Ann. Mag. nat. Hist.* Ser. 2, **15**: 410
Oligolophis palpinalis: Simon, 1879: *Les Arachnides de France* **7**: 248
Odiellus palpinalis: Roewer, 1923: *Weberknechte der Erde:* 728
Lophopilio palpinalis: Šilhavý, 1956: *Fauna ČSR:* 214

Diagnosis: Palpal claw present but without pectination. Trident conspicuous; central member longest. Distinguished from all others by the form of its strongly armed pedipalp (Fig. 28C). Penis distinct (see below and Fig. 28D).

Body length: male 2.8–3.8 mm, female 3.5–5.0 mm

Length of second leg: 12.0–15.0 mm

Body (Fig. 28A) rather short, dull yellow or reddish brown. Saddle usually present, well-marked on cephalothorax and followed on abdomen by pairs of dark brown patches on each tergite as far as tergite 6. Ocularium (Fig. 28B) slightly wider than long, about one and a half times its length distant from front margin of cephalothorax and with two rows of three to five rather blunt tubercles on top. Trident conspicuous, set at about 50° and with central member longer than laterals. Openings of odoriferous glands small. Abdomen smooth, without tuberculations.

Chelicerae pale brown, shaped normally but relatively robust.

Pedipalps (Figs. 28B, C) strongly armed: trochanter, femur and tibia with conspicuous ventral spine-tipped tubercles. Femur, patella (Fig. 28B, arrowed) and sometimes tibia each with a distal apophysis on inner side; apophyses furnished with hairs. Tarsus provided with many spines.

Legs rather short, yellow brown and vaguely annulated; femora rounded, patellae and tibiae angular in cross-section.

Penis (Fig. 28D): corpus slender but base broad; stylus rather twisted.

Occurrence. A species widely distributed in Great Britain but not recorded from Ireland. Possibly it is most common in central and eastern England but nowhere is it ever very numerous. It appears to have a preference for the ground layer of deciduous woodland, undisturbed hedgerows and gardens. In Holland it has been recorded from dry open places covered with lichens (Spoek, 1963). Adults may be found from July to January. Eggs are laid in late summer and autumn, they hatch during the following spring. Juveniles occur from May until October.

Type locality. Briesnitz, Poland. The first British record (sub *Opilio terricola* Koch)) was by Meade (1855) after examining a specimen sent by J. Blackwall from North Wales. (Map 21, p. 108) Abroad the species occurs in central Europe from eastern France to southern Sweden and Bulgaria. It ascends to an altitude of 1700 m in the Alps (Martens, 1978).

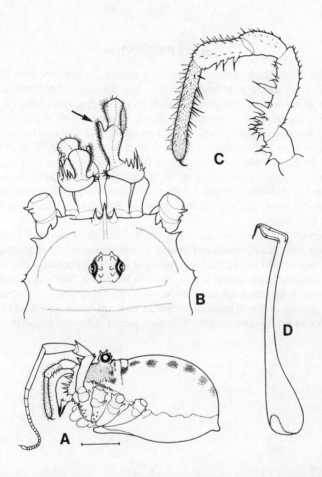

Fig. 28. *Lophopilio palpinalis*. A. Lateral view of female body with pedipalp and leg 1 (bar = 1 mm); B. Dorsal view of cephalothorax with pedipalps showing apophysis on patella (arrowed); C. Outside lateral view of left male pedipalp; D. Lateral view of penis.

Family LEIOBUNIDAE

The legs of leiobunids are usually very long and slender while the body is small. In British species the body length reaches about 6 mm; usually there is a saddle pattern on the dorsum. The eyes are raised on a distinct ocularium but the trident is absent. Generally, body armature is little developed but rows of denticles on the leg coxae occur in some genera (e.g. *Leiobunum*). The supra-cheliceral lamella lacks denticles. The openings of the odoriferous glands are visible from above.

The tarsus of the pedipalp is longer than the tibia and a terminal claw is present; the claw is pectinate. Depending on the subfamily an apophysis on the pedipalp is present (Gyantinae) or absent (Leiobuninae). The basal segment of the chelicera has a ventral spine. The coxae of the legs are not fixed; the maxillary lobe of coxa 2 is well-developed.

The ovipositor is long and multi-segmented. The form of the penis is variable: relatively stout in *Leiobunum* and *Nelima* with glans and corpus (including distal keel structure) held in a straight line; but more slender in *Dicranopalpus ramosus* where a distinct glans is held at an angle with the corpus (keel structure absent).

Leiobunids are characteristic of the shrub layer. The family, comprising about twenty genera, occurs in the north temperate zone and in the New World tropics. The four British species are placed in three genera and two subfamilies.

Key to Species of the Leiobunidae (adults)

1. Patella of pedipalp with an apophysis at least half the length of the tibia (arrowed).

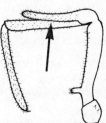

....*Dicranopalpus ramosus* (p. 92)

Patella of pedipalp without an apophysis **2**

2. Leg 2 not normally less than 40.0 mm in length. Coxae furnished with a series of minute denticles (high magnification) on each side (arrowed, see also Fig. 30B). Trochanters mostly dark, contrasting with coxae. Ocularium smooth

....**3**

Leg 2 not normally more than 40.0 mm in length. Coxae without rows of denticles. Trochanters pale, not contrasting with coxae. Ocularium with short denticles and setae best seen in lateral view (arrowed)

....*Nelima gothica* (p. 98)

3. Each eye surrounded by a white ring (arrowed); dark between the rings (dorsal view)

....*Leiobunum blackwalli* (p. 96)

Each eye surrounded by a black ring (arrowed); pale between the rings (dorsal view)

....*Leiobunum rotundum* (p. 94)

Dicranopalpus ramosus (Simon)
(Fig. 29)

Dicranochirus ramosus Simon, 1909: *Mems R. Soc. esp. Hist. nat.* **6**: 43
Dicranopalpus caudatus Dresco, 1948: *Bull. Mus. natn. Hist. nat. Paris* 2
ser., **20** (4): 336
D. ramosus: Starega, 1973: *Annls zool. Warsz.* **30**: 362

Diagnosis: Palpal claw present, with pectination. Trident absent. Distinguished from all others by the form of the pedipalp: very long and with an exceptional apophysis on the patella (Figs. 29A, B). Penis distinct (see below and Figs. 29D, E).

Body length: male 3.0–4.0 mm, female 4.0–6.0 mm
Length of second leg: 40.0–50.0 mm

Body (Figs. 29A, C) extremely variable in colouration. Females often greyish brown with one or more dark transverse bars and a rather vague pale median longitudinal stripe. Males in particular may have a strikingly marked black saddle on a silvery-yellow, black-spotted dorsum. Entire abdomen smooth but females usually have a posterior protuberance (tergites 5 and 6) best seen in lateral view (Fig. 29C). Ocularium silvery, somewhat wider than long and slightly less than its length distant from anterior margin of cephalothorax. Trident absent. Openings of odoriferous glands small.

Chelicerae pale brown, rather prominent and armed with a number of hair-tipped tubercles.

Pedipalps (Figs. 29A, B) very long and conspicuous and provided with two apophyses: one at base of femur and a second on inner surface of patella. Apophysis on female patella almost as thick and long as tibia; in male (Fig. 29B, arrowed) relatively short and slender. Pedipalps have dark markings on tibia, patella and apophysis. Tarsal claw pectinate (see p. 39).

Legs long, strongly annulated yellow and brown but little armed. Typically, at rest, legs held in laterigrade position (right angles to body).

Penis (Figs. 29D, E): stylus short but with many small setae; glans almost as broad as long.

Occurrence. Since its British discovery at Bournemouth in 1957 this species has established many thriving colonies in the south. At present it is known to occur in lowland localities (up to 160 m at Bath, Brown (1984) south of a line from Cardigan Bay to the Orwell; usually it is not far from the coast. In this country *Dicranopalpus* is mostly synanthropic in its choice of habitat. It has a marked preference for gardens and hedges, occurring in particular on Holm oak (*Quercus ilex*) and conifers. Beating the foliage is the best method of collection. Adults have been recorded from August to November; eggs resulting from this generation overwinter to hatch the following May and June. Immatures, recognizable by their even more obvious palpal apophyses, tend to occur in the ground layer.

93

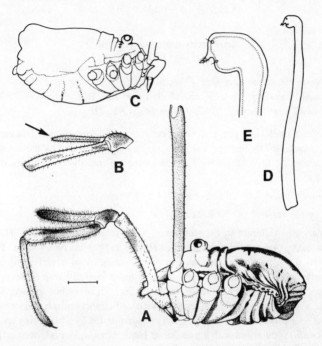

Fig. 29. *Dicranopalpus ramosus*. A. Lateral view of female body with femur of leg 1 and pedipalp showing apophysis on patella (bar = 1 mm); B. Outside lateral view of male pedipalp tibia and patella showing apophysis (arrowed); C. Lateral view of female body showing 'tailed' variety of abdomen; D. Lateral view of penis; E. Lateral view of glans penis.

Type locality. Mogador, Morocco. The first British record (Sankey & Storey, 1969) was by E. Rix at Bournemouth in 1957. (Map 22, p. 109) Abroad the species is known from its type locality; the Serra da Estrêla (Portugal); the region of Les Landes in S.W. France; and most importantly, the east coast of Spain from Murcia north to the Pyrenées Orientales (France). In this region it occurs from sea level to over 1000 m (Rambla, 1986).

Remarks. Brown (1984) has bred *Dicranopalpus* through its complete life cycle. As a result of breeding experiments, Brown (pers. comm.) found that the dorsal pattern exhibited distinct polymorphisms. When crossed, striped and non-striped varieties showed easily obtained segregation.

Leiobunum rotundum (Latreille)
(Figs. 30 & 31)

Phalangium rotundum Latreille, 1798: *Bull. Sci. Soc. Philom.* **1**: 113
Leiobunum rotundum: C. L. Koch, 1839: *Über. des Arachnidensyst.* **2**: 36
Nelima fuscifrons: Sankey, 1953: *Entomologist* **86**: 116

Diagnosis: Palpal claw present, with pectination. Trident absent. Distinguished from *L. blackwalli* (p. 96) by its larger size, its longer legs and by the colouration of its ocularium (eye surrounded by dark ring). Penis distinct (see below and Fig. 30C).

Body length: male 3.0–4.0 mm, female 4.5–6.5 mm

Length of second leg: 50.0–60.0 mm

Body markedly different in the two sexes. Male relatively small (Fig. 31A) and uniform orange or reddish brown with only the suggestion of a saddle. Female (Fig. 31B) dorsum brown with gold or silver patches and usually with a dark rectangular saddle. Female abdomen often suffused laterally with pink or red in fresh specimens. Trident and armature absent in both sexes but surface of body granular. Ocularium slightly longer than wide and almost entirely smooth except for about four tiny spincules on top. Each eye surrounded by a black ring (compare *L. blackwalli*); ocularium with a pale dorsal band. Openings of odoriferous glands inconspicuous. Supra-cheliceral lamella forms a pair of projections as seen from above. Ventrum of female pale yellow brown.

Chelicerae relatively weak, pale coloured, basal segment with a ventral spur.

Pedipalps (Fig. 30B) pale with dark patches and only lightly armed. Tarsal claw pectinate (see p. 39).

Legs exceptionally long and slender (Fig. 30A) and mostly dark brown or black but coxae pale with white joints. In lateral or ventral view coxae edged with rows of minute bifid or trifid denticles (Fig. 30B, arrowed). Femora with rows of acute tubercles.

Penis (Fig. 30C): corpus longer and narrower than in *L. blackwalli* Fig. 30D); keel structure on distal section of corpus shaped differently in the two species.

Occurrence. Widely distributed in the British Isles and one of our most abundant species especially in the south. It occurs in natural and man-made habitats. It inhabits all kinds of woods, heaths, gardens and hedgerows but is usually scarce on dunes and open grasslands. Adults are generally found on shrubs, bushes, trees and walls (sometimes in groups) but the species may also be taken in pitfall traps and at carrion. After hatching from eggs in April and May the immatures remain in or near the ground layer. Adults appear from late July and some individuals may survive until the beginning of December.

Type locality. Brive (central France). The first British record was by Meade (1855) who described it as 'very abundant'. (Map 23, p. 109) Abroad the species is

95

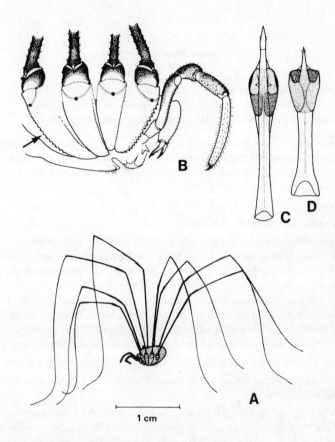

Fig. 30. *Leiobunum rotundum*. A. Whole animal; B. Lateral, partly ventral, view of pedipalp and coxae showing series of denticulae (arrowed). [For dorsal views see Fig. 31] C. Ventral view of penis. *Leiobunum blackwalli*. D. Ventral view of penis. [Both penes drawn to scale.]

distributed throughout most of Europe, excepting the Mediterranean Region, to Russia and to 62°N in Scandinavia. It occurs up to 2000 m in the Alps (Martens, 1978).

Leiobunum blackwalli Meade
(Figs. 30 & 31)

Leiobunus blackwallii Meade, 1861: *Ann. Mag. nat. Hist.* Ser. 3, **7**: 355
Liobunum blackwalli: Simon, 1879: *Les Arachnides de France* **7**: 178
Leiobunum blackwalli: Todd, 1948: *Entomologist's mon. Mag.* **84**: 111

Diagnosis: Palpal claw present, with pectination. Trident absent. Distinguished from *L. rotundum* (p. 94) by the colouration of its ocularium (eye surrounded by pale ring) and from *Nelima gothica* by its trochanters with dark markings (Figs. 31C, D). Penis distinct (see below and Fig. 30D).

Body length: 2.6–3.6 mm, female 4.0–6.0 mm

Length of second leg: 40.0–50.0 mm

Body markedly different in the two sexes. Female (Fig. 31C) dorsum pale silvery brown usually with a darker saddle. Saddle widens posteriorly and terminates abruptly on tergite 4. Male (Fig. 31D) relatively small and pale orange brown with only the suggestion of a saddle. Trident and armature absent in both sexes but surface of body granular. Ocularium slightly longer than wide and virtually smooth with a dark median band; each eye surrounded by a white ring (compare *L. rotundum*). Openings of odoriferous glands inconspicuous. Supra-cheliceral lamella forms a pair of projections as seen from above. Ventrum pale coloured in both sexes.

Chelicerae rather weak, pale coloured, basal segment with a ventral spur.

Pedipalps pale coloured but darker on tarsus. Pedipalps only lightly armed, tarsal claw pectinate (see p. 39).

Legs very long and slender, lighter in ground colour than *L. rotundum*. Viewed laterally or ventrally coxae edged with rows of minute bifid or trifid denticles as in Fig. 30B (arrowed) – sometimes visible only with difficulty. Femora with rows of acute tubercles.

Penis (Fig. 30D): corpus shorter and broader than in *L. rotundum* (Fig. 30C); keel structure on distal section of corpus shaped differently in the two species.

Occurrence. Widely distributed in the British Isles but scarce in the north; less frequent than *L. rotundum*. It is essentially a woodland species and its preference appears to be for deciduous woodland with well developed field and shrub layers. However, it may also occur in relatively open habitats such as heathland, grassland and hedgerow. Adults may be found on tree trunks and low foliage; the young stages remain in the ground layer. Adults appear from July onwards and some individuals may survive until January; eggs laid during this period hatch mostly in May.

Type locality. England. Meade (1861) mentioned no particular locality in describing this species which is named after J. Blackwall who first called attention to its distinction. (Map 24, p. 109) Abroad the species is widespread in Europe as far north as southern Sweden but excluding the Mediterranean Region. It occurs up to 800 m in the Alps but it is not recorded from Austria or Hungary (Martens, 1978).

97

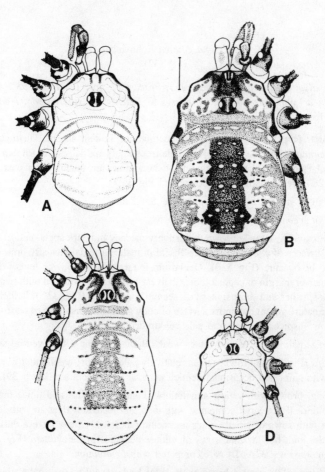

Fig. 31. *Leiobunum rotundum*. A. Dorsal view of male body with pedipalp and bases of legs;
B. Dorsal view of female body with pedipalp and bases of legs (bar = 1 mm). *Leiobunum
blackwalli*. C. Dorsal view of female body with pedipalp and bases of legs; D. Dorsal view
of male body with pedipalp and bases of legs. [All Figs. drawn to scale.]

98

Nelima gothica Lohmander
(Fig. 32)

Nelima silvatica (part): Bristowe, 1935: *Proc. zool. Soc. Lond.* **2**: 233
N. gothica Lohmander, 1945: *Göteborgs K. Vetensk.-o. vitterhSamh. Handl.* **3**
  (9): 16

Diagnosis: Palpal claw present, with pectination. Trident absent. Distinguished
from *Leiobunum* by the shorter legs, pale trochanters and lack of coxal denticles.
The ocularium has a characteristic line of short spines and spicules above each eye
(Fig. 32C). Penis distinct (see below and Fig. 32D).

Body length: male 2.5–3.5 mm, female 3.5–4.5 mm

Length of second leg: 30.0–40.0 mm

Body (Figs. 32A, B) pale brown with silvery patches and dark spots on dorsal and
lateral surfaces of abdomen. Saddle absent in male; in female usually present but
tends to be obscure (Fig. 32B). Ocularium longer than wide, one length distant
from anterior margin of cephalothorax, silvery on top and furnished with two rows
of black spicules and short spines best seen in lateral view (Fig. 32C). Trident and
other armature absent but entire surface of body granular. Openings of odoriferous
glands inconspicuous. Ventrum pale coloured.

Chelicerae pale coloured and rather weak. Basal segment with a ventral spur.

Pedipalps (Fig. 32A) brown, tarsus relatively pale. Femur, patella and tibia provided with hairs and occasional denticles; tarsal claw pectinate (see p. 39).

Legs long, brown with yellow annulations. Femora, patellae and tibiae more or
less cylindrical and stout compared with tarsi and metatarsi (less so with leg 2).
Femora with rows of small spines and acute tubercles. Coxae have a dark spot
below the joint but lack the rows of minute denticles in *Leiobunum* (Fig. 30B).
Trochanters (Figs. 32A, B) pale compared with *Leiobunum*.

Penis (Fig. 32D): corpus broad with distal keel structure, the shape of which
differs from *Leiobunum*.

Occurrence. This species has a wide distribution but the records are rather sparse
and from quite divergent habitats. It appears to have a preference for the coast,
especially in the west and NE, and it has been recorded from a number of offshore
islands. Usually *Nelima* is found in coarse grassland, tangled vegetation or under
stones, wood and debris (Brown & Sankey, 1949). In London it has been collected
from a bramble patch beside the Western Region main railway line. In the Pen-
nines it is known from a number of localities above 300 metres. Adults occur from
July until the frosts; eggs from this generation hatch the following spring.

Type locality. Gotland and Öland (Scandinavia). The first British record was by
W. S. Bristowe (1935) from the islands of Skokholm, Grassholm and May. (Map
25, p. 109) Abroad there are three centres of distribution: N. Spain and the
Pyrenees, the Paris Basin and the western Baltic region (Martens, 1978).

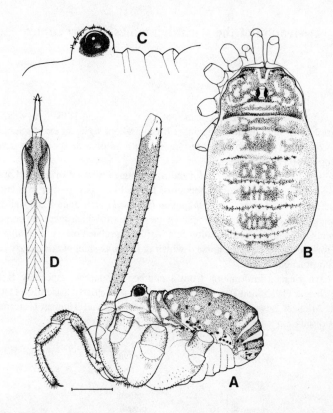

Fig. 32. *Nelima gothica*. A. Lateral view of male body with pedipalp and femur of leg 1 (bar = 1 mm); B. Dorsal view of female body; C. Lateral view of dorsal surface of cephalothorax showing short setae and tubercles on ocularium; D. Ventral view of penis.

Derivation of the scientific names of harvestmen

A study of the origin of scientific names of living organisms is likely to encounter many difficulties and obscure meanings. It cannot hope to be an exact science for only recently has it become the custom for authors of new species to give an etymology in their publications.

Usually scientific names are latinized and frequently their origin is Latin or Greek. Some names are given in honour of fellow biologists, past or present, and such are called *patronyms*, e.g. *Leiobunum blackwalli* after John Blackwall FLS, an eminent 19th century arachnologist. A *metanym*, of which there are some examples in Opiliones, is a substitution of a word by a related one, e.g. *ephippios* – Greek for something put on a horse – which in *Lacinius ephippiatus* clearly refers to the conspicuous saddle.

We have gleaned information from a number of sources, especially Holmes (1979), Jaeger (1955) and Parker (1982). We are particularly grateful to Douglas Brown, Michael Edwards, Professor Jochen Martens and Thomas Usborne for helpful discussion with certain names. (L) = Latin, (G) = Greek.

Name	Construction	Meaning
agrestis	*agrestis* (L)	rural
Anelasmocephalus	*an*	without
	elasmos } (G)	plated
	kephalos	head
bimaculatum	*bis* } (L)	twice
	macula	spot
blackwalli	Dr J. Blackwall	patronym
Boeorix	*baios* or *boeos* (G)	slight, or of an ox; the connection is obscure
cambridgei	Rev. O. Pickard-Cambridge	patronym
chrysomelas	*chrysos* } (G)	gold
	melas	dark
Cyphophthalmi	*kyphos* } (G)	humped ⎫ refers presumably to the odoriferous glands placed
	opthalmos	eye ⎬ on tubercles; they have the appearance of eyes
diadema	*diadem* (G)	royal fillet or crown
Dicranopalpus	*dicranos* } (G)	two headed pedipalp
	palpus	
ephippiatus	*ephippios* (G)	metanym, refers to something put on a horse, i.e. a saddle
ericaeus	*erike* (G)	heather
gothica	*gothicus* (L)	a native of Gotland, Sweden

Name	Construction	Meaning
hanseni	H. J. Hansen	patronym
Homalenotus	*homalos* } (G) *noton*	smooth or level back
Lacinius	*lacinia* (L)	something torn or the lapel of a garment; refers perhaps to strong spination
Laniatores	*lanio* } (L) *tor*	to tear in pieces } refers to the the doer of an action } large claws on } the pedipalp
Leiobunum	*leios* } (G) *bounos*	smooth eminence, bump or mound
Lophopilio	*lophos* (G) *opilio* (L)	crest, ridge or nape shepherd } perhaps the making of a new genus by uniting syllables from two existing genera, i.e. *Oligolophus* and *Opilio*
manducus	*manducus* (L)	glutton, or queer chewing figure; the meaning is obscure
meadii	R. M. Meade	patronym
Megabunus	*mega* } (G) *bounos*	large eminence, bump or mound
Mitopus	*mitos* } (G) *pous*	thread foot (leg)
Mitostoma	*mitos* } (G) *stoma*	thread mouth
morio	*morion* (L) or possibly *mor* (Celtic)	fool, monster } meaning obscure black }
Nelima	*ne* } (G) *lima*	not roughened
Nemastoma	*nema* } (G) *stoma*	thread mouth
Odiellus	*odios* (G)	belonging to a way or a journey; perhaps refers to a roadside habitat
Oligolophus	*oligos* } (G) *lophos*	small crest, ridge or nape
Opilio	*opilio* (L)	shepherd (see *Introduction*)
Palpatores	*palpo* } (L) *tor*	to feel one's way or } refers to the stroke the doer of an } use of the action } pedipalps
palpinalis	*palpo* (L)	see above
parietinus	*paries* (L)	wall; occurring on a wall
Paroligolophus	*par* (G) *Oligolophus*	near or related to see above

Name	Construction	Meaning
Phalangium	*phalangion* or *phalangos* } (G)	spider finger segment or joint
quadridentatus	*quadra* *dens* } (L)	four tooth
ramblaianum	Dr M. Rambla	patronym
ramosus	*ramus* (L)	branch; refers to the apophyses on the pedipalps or possibly to the legs which spread out laterally when at rest
Rilaena	Rila Mountains, Bulgaria	Type species locality
rotundum	*rotundus* (L)	round
Sabacon	*saos* (G) *baca* (L)	safe, healthy } berry } probably refers to the well developed segments of the pedipalps
saxatilis	*saxum* (L)	stone; living among stones
spinosus	*spina* (L)	thorn
triangularis	*tria* *angulus* } (L)	three angle
tricarinatus	*tria* *carina* } (L)	three keel or ridge
tridens	*tria* *dens* } (L)	three tooth
Trogulus	*trogo* or *trogl* } (G) *lus*	to gnaw or a hole made by gnawing (diminutive form) } perhaps a dweller in a small hole or an inhabitant of soil
viscayanum	Viscaya in Spain	Type locality

Distribution maps of the species

Although many unrecorded areas remain, especially in Ireland, general patterns are clear. There is a decrease in the diversity of the British harvest-spider fauna northward. From the species maps, this is to be expected, as several species are predominantly southern in range, whereas only two (*Oligolophus hanseni* and the recently described *Mitopus ericaeus*) are more frequent in northern Britain than in the south.

The distribution of squares in which high numbers of species have been recorded is interesting. In the south of England, these squares lie mainly on calcareous soils, the chalk of the North and South Downs being apparent. The reason may be that several species, such as the trogulids and *Homalenotus* are most often found there. Indeed, it is only in sites where calcareous grassland and woodland meet that over 20 species of harvest-spider are regularly found.

The few squares in the north which exceed 15 species are nearly all areas of mature sand dunes or lowland sandy heath, where outlying populations of such species as *Paroligolophus meadii*, *Opilio saxatilis* and *Nelima gothica* have been found (see also *Distribution and Ecology*, p. 22–27).

We would like to thank all those who have contributed to the Biological Recording Scheme for harvestmen. This includes personnel of colleges, museums, the Nature Conservancy Council and the Institute of Terrestrial Ecology as well as some 140 individuals. From their records, Paul Harding and Brian Eversham of the Monks Wood Experimental Station have produced distribution maps for all species. We gratefully acknowledge the kind permission of the Institute of Terrestrial Ecology to use these maps in this *Synopsis*.

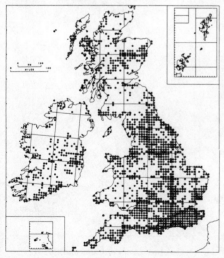

Map 1 **Coverage map**

All harvestmen species

✳ = 1–7 species recorded

● = 8–15 species recorded

■ = 16 or more species recorded

104

Maps 2–25 Species maps

The three symbols show the date of the most recent record of a species from a 10 km square:

○ = up to 1929
● = 1930–1969
■ = 1970–1985

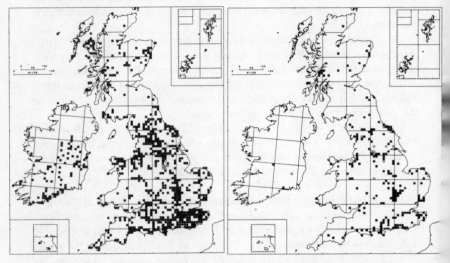

2. *Nemastoma bimaculatum*

3. *Mitostoma chrysomelas*

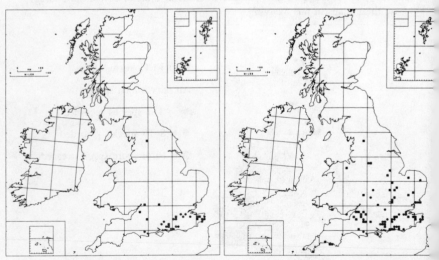

4. *Trogulus tricarinatus*

5. *Anelasmocephalus cambridgei*

Maps 6–9

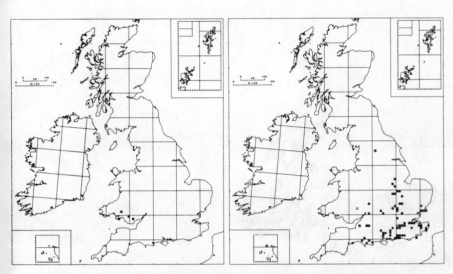

6. *Sabacon viscayanum ramblaianum*   7. *Homalenotus quadridentatus*

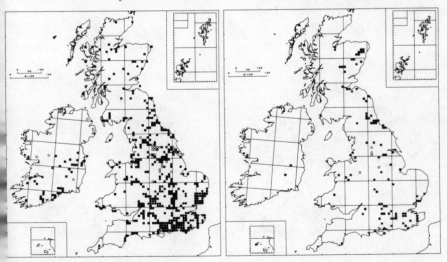

8. *Oligolophus tridens*   9. *Oligolophus hanseni*

Maps 10–13

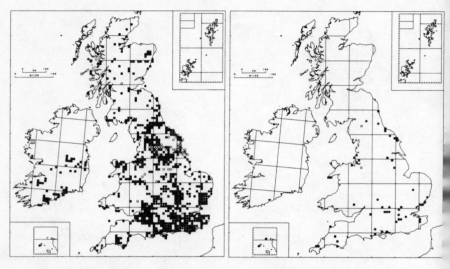

10. *Paroligolophus agrestis*   11. *Paroligolophus meadii*

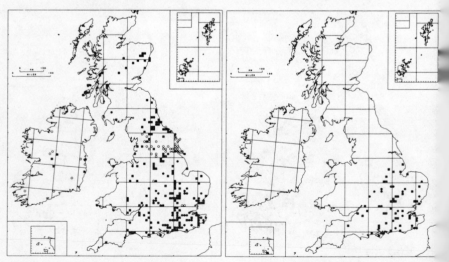

12. *Lacinius ephippiatus*   13. *Odiellus spinosus*

Maps 14–17

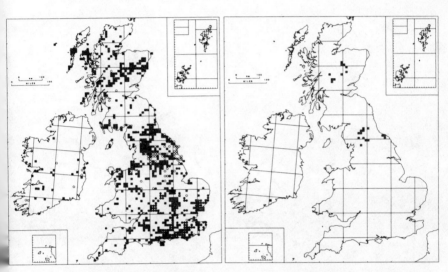

14. *Mitopus morio*   15. *Mitopus morio* variety *ericaeus*

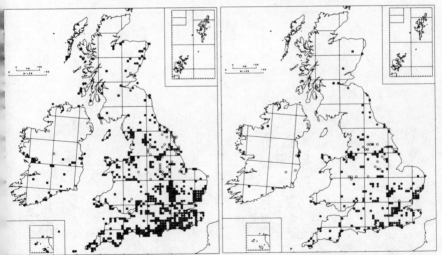

16. *Phalangium opilio*   17. *Opilio parietinus*

Maps 18–21

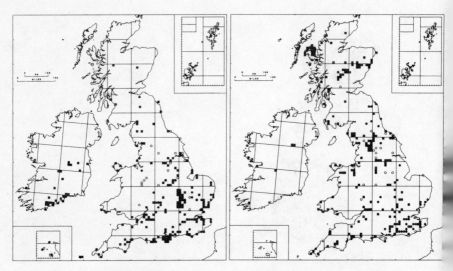

18. *Opilio saxatilis* 19. *Megabunus diadema*

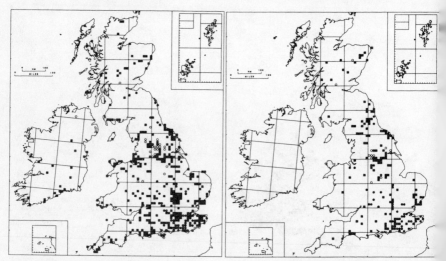

20. *Rilaena triangularis* 21. *Lophopilio palpinalis*

Maps 22–25

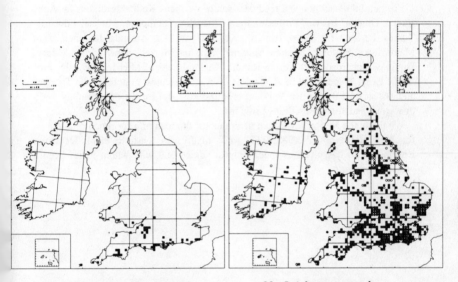

22. *Dicranopalpus ramosus*   23. *Leiobunum rotundum*

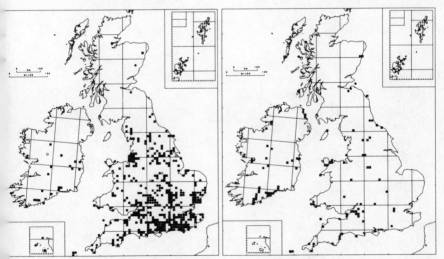

24. *Leiobunum blackwalli*   25. *Nelima gothica*

110

Acknowledgements

For helpful discussion and ready assistance we thank Keith Alexander, Dr Anne Baker, Douglas Brown, Professor John Cloudsley-Thompson, Michael Edwards, Teresa Farino, Dr Steve Hopkin, Keith Hyatt, Dr Amanda Jennings, Don Macfarlane, Professor Jochen Martens, Cynthia Merrett, Dr Andrew Milner, Douglas Richardson, Dr Adrian Rundle, Dr Paul Selden, Michael Tweedie, Professor Erika Wagner and Fred Wanless. We are also most grateful to the Trustees and Director of the British Museum (Natural History) for the opportunbity to do this work and for the facilities provided.

We thank the National Museum of Wales for the loan of a specimen of *Sabacon* for illustration (no. Z 1985.111). And, finally, we wish to thank Dr Doris Kermack who has given us much helpful advice and with whom it has been a pleasure to work.

Glossary

Abdomen In arthropods, the posterior region of the body derived from a series of similar segments.

Anal aperture The posterior opening of the alimentary canal through which the faeces are voided. It is surrounded by the anal operculum or anal plate, the modified tenth tergite.

Apodeme An infolding of the cuticle serving as an attachment for muscles.

Apophysis A branch or extension.

Apotele An articulating, claw-like structure.

Armature A collective term for the structures occurring on the exoskeleton such as spines, tubercles and denticles.

Astragulus Basal division of a metatarsus.

Autotomy The voluntary shedding of a limb, usually to escape from a predator.

Bifid Of a structure, branched into two parts.

Calcaneus Distal division of a metatarsus.

Calcareous Of the soil, rich in basic salts especially calcium.

Camerostome In Trogulidae, the cavity enclosing the mouthparts.

Capitate Of setae, tipped with a glandular secretion.

Carapace The somewhat toughened, dorsal section of the cephalothorax.

Cephalothorax In Arachnida, that part of the body, anterior to the abdomen, in which the head is fused to the thorax.

Chelicera (pl. Chelicerae) One of a pair of pincer-like appendages on the cephalothorax used in feeding.

Cheliceral gland A gland found in the chelicera of adult males of the families Nemastomatidae and Sabaconidae; used in pheromone communication.

Clypeus see **Epistome**.

Corpus Of the penis: the trunk or chief part.

Coxa The basal segment of legs and pedipalp.

Coxapophysis (pl. Coxapophyses) An apophysis on the inner side of the coxa associated with feeding.

Coxisternal feeding Feeding in which food is torn into small pieces by the mouth-parts and anterior legs, taken into the mouth and digested internally.

Cucullus see **Hood**.

Cuticle A layer covering, and secreted by, the epidermis; the outer layer of the integument.

Denticle A short, solid outgrowth of the cuticle.

Distal Furthest from the body (syn. apical).

Dorsal shield A fused, sclerotized and strengthened region of the dorsum.

Dorsum The dorsal or upper surface of the body.

Ecdysis The periodic shedding of the exoskeleton to allow for growth (moulting).

Eclosion The emergence of the young from the egg.

Epistome The part of the pre-cheliceral material lying between cephalic lobe and labrum, also known as the clypeus.

Exocrine Of glands possessing a duct carrying secretions to the surface.

Extrinsic muscles Muscles which originate distally of the organ to which they are attached.

112

Femur (pl. **Femora**) The third segment of legs and pedipalp occurring between trochanter and patella.

Genital opening The opening through which pass the extrusible reproductive organs; they are covered, at rest, by the genital operculum.

Genital operculum A fold of tissue which encloses the reproductive organs at rest. It is sealed in the immature but opens anteriorly in the adult (genital opening).

Glans Of the penis, the section which bears the stylus.

Gnathobase Maxillary lobe.

Gravid Refers to a female swollen with eggs.

Haemocoel The main body cavity; a blood filled expansion of the blood vascular system.

Hair A general term for a very fine, non-erect spine.

Hirsute Hairy, shaggy.

Homeostasis The (close up) maintenance of the chemical and physiological properties of the body at a constant state.

Hood In Trogulidae, the cephalic extension covering the pedipalps and mouthparts. Also known as the **cucullus**.

Instar The stage of life between any two ecdyses (moults). A variable number of instars occur before maturity.

Integument The organism's outer protective covering including the cuticle.

Intrinsic muscles Muscles which originate proximally to the organ to which they are attached.

Intromittent Descriptive of a male organ inserted into the female genital opening to transfer sperm.

Lamella see Supra-cheliceral lamella.

Labium The modified maxilla, also known as the lower lip, which assists in feeding.

Labrum The part of the pre-cheliceral material lying beyond the epistome.

Lentigen cells In the eye, the cells positioned between the lens and the retina.

Lyrifissure A minute slit in the cuticle which by means of its neural connection acts as a mechanoreceptor. Groups of lyrifissures are known as lyriform organs.

Lyriform organ see **Lyrifissure**.

Maxillary lobe An apophysis on the coxa of leg or pedipalp associated with feeding.

Mesopeltidium The dorsal sclerite formed by the fifth cephalic segment.

Metapeltidium The dorsal sclerite formed by the sixth cephalic segment.

Metatarsus (pl. **Metatarsi**) The sixth leg segment occurring between tibia and tarsus; absent in pedipalp.

Myliosoma The mouthparts together with those parts of the appendages involved in feeding.

Nominate In taxonomy, used of a subordinate taxon (subspecies or subgenus) containing the type of the higher taxon and bearing the same name.

Ocularium A mound-like structure bearing the eyes (≡ **ocular tubercule**).

Odoriferous gland A gland producing noxious fluid to repel enemies; the fluid is expelled through the pair of openings on the sides of the carapace (ozopores) (≡ **repugnatorial glands**).

Opisthosoma The body behind, i.e. the abdomen.

Ovipositor The female tubular organ used to deposit eggs in the substrate; when withdrawn it lies behind the genital operculum.

Parthenogenesis Reproduction in which the eggs develop without fertilization by the male.

Patella (pl. **Patellae**) The fourth segment occurring between femur and tibia of legs and pedipalp.

Pectinate Like a comb; having pectination or teeth.

Pedipalp (or palp) One of a pair of leg-like appendages on the cephalothorax, used in the manipulation of food etc.

Penis The distal part of the male reproductive apparatus, used to transfer sperm; when withdrawn it lies behind the genital operculum.

Pharynx The region of the alimentary canal just posterior to the mouth.

Phylogenetic A classification based on phylogeny, i.e. on evolutionary descent.

Polymorphic Two or more different forms of individuals in the same species; not sexual differences.

Pre-cheliceral see **Prosomatic material**.

Propeltidium The anterior region of the carapace derived from the first four cephalic segments.

Prosoma The first part of the body, i.e. the cephalothorax.

Prosomatic material Material primitively anterior to the six cephalic segments, now fused with the cephalothorax; also known as pre-cheliceral material.

Proximal Nearest to the body (syn. basal).

Respiratory stigma (pl. **stigmata**) Aperture situated close to posterior edge of coxa 4.

Rickettsia Intracellular, prokaryotic parasites which can multiply only within their arthropod hosts. They are considered to be intermediate between bacteria and viruses.

Saddle A central, longitudinal pattern on the dorsum characteristic of many species in the families Phalangiidae and Leiobunidae.

Sclerite A part of the cuticle hardened for skeletal function; the cuticle between sclerites usually remains flexible to allow movement.

Sclerotized Hardened to form a sclerite by a process of tanning the protein of the cuticle.

Scutum A tough, sclerotized covering formed by the consolidation of any number of dorsal elements.

Seta (pl. **Setae**) An erect, hollow, hair-like projection of the cuticle enclosing part of an epidermal cell.

Simple eye An eye in which a single lens covers a group of light sensitive cells.

Somatic The non-reproductive part of the body.

Spicule A small, erect denticle.

Spine A bristle-like structure which communicates with a nerve ending.

Spiracle An external opening for tracheae.

Spur Cheliceral spur: the ventral tubercle on the basal joint of the chelicera of some species; usually it is pointed in lateral view but its prominence varies. It may be necessary to remove the chelicera to see the spur.

Sternite The ventral part of each abdominal segment.

Sternum A plate on the ventral surface of the cephalothorax; usually obscured by the coxae in Opiliones.

Stigma (pl. **stigmata**) One of a pair of large tracheal openings on the ventrum.

Stridulation The production of sound usually by rubbing one part of the body against another.

Stylus Of the penis, the distal prolongation of the glans; it may resemble a short needle.

Supra-cheliceral lamella A fold of tissue lying between the anterior margin of the carapace and the bases of the chelicerae.

Synanthropic *lit.* together with man; distribution relates to human settlement.

Tarsus (pl. **Tarsi**) The terminal segment of legs and pedipalp.

Tergite The dorsal part of each abdominal segment.

Tibia (pl. **Tibiae**) The fifth segment of legs and pedipalp.

Trachea (pl. **Tracheae**) Branching invagination of the body wall through which air diffuses directly to the tissues.

Trident A close group of three tubercles in the centre of the anterior edge of the carapace, characteristic of the family Phalangiidae.

Trochanter The second segment of legs and pedipalp occurring between coxa and femur.

Tubercle A hollow projection of the cuticle.

Trifid Of a structure, branched into three parts.

Ventrum The under or lower surface of the body.

References

Abbott, R. H. R. 1981. A new opilionid to Great Britain. *Newsl. Br. arachnol. Soc.* **30**, 4.

Adams, J. 1984. The habitat and feeding ecology of woodland harvestmen (Opiliones) in England. *Oikos* **42** (3), 361–370.

Barth, F. G. and Stagl, J., 1976. The slit sense organs of arachnids. A comparative study of their topography on the walking legs (Chelicerata, Arachnida). *Zoomorphologie* **86**, 1–23.

Bragg, P. D. and Holmberg, R. G. 1974. *Platybunus triangularis* and *Paroligolophus agrestis*: Two phalangids introduced into North America (Arachnida, Opiliones). *J. arachnol.* **2** (2), 127.

Bristowe, W. S. 1935. The spiders of Skokholm (S. Wales), with notes on a phalangid new to Britain. *Proc. zool. Soc. Lond.* **3**, 233–239.

Bristowe, W. S. 1941. *The Comity of Spiders*. Vol. 2, 324–325. London, Ray Society.

Bristowe, W. S. 1949. The distribution of harvestmen (Phalangida) in Great Britain and Ireland with notes on their names, enemies and food. *J. anim. Ecol.* **18** (1), 100–114.

Brown, D. G. and Sankey, J. H. P. 1949. The harvest-spider *Nelima silvatica* (Simon) in Great Britain, *Proc. zool. Soc. Lond.* **114**, 867–871.

Brown, D. G. 1984. Observations on the distribution and life-cycle of *Dicranopalpus ramosus* (Simon, 1909), Opiliones. *Newsl. Br. arachnol. Soc.* **40**, 7–8.

Cloudsley-Thompson, J. L. 1988. *Evolution and adaptation of terrestrial arthropods.* 141 pp. Springer-Verlag Berlin Heidelberg.

Cokendolpher, J. C. 1986. A new species of fossil *Pellobunus* from Dominican Republic amber (Arachnida: Opiliones: Phalangodidae). *Carib. J. Sci.* **22** (3–4), 205–211.

Cottam, C. 1949. Quoted by Bristowe, 1949.

Curtis, D. J. 1970. Comparative aspects of the fine structure of the eyes of Phalangiidae (Arachnida) and certain correlations with habitat. *J. zool. Res.* **160**, 231–265.

Dalingwater, J. 1983. IX International Congress of Arachnology, Panama, August 1983. *Newsl. Br. arachnol. Soc.* **38**, 2–4.

Dresco, D. 1948. Remarques sur le genre *Dicranopalpus* Dol. et description de deux espèces nouvelles (Opiliones). *Bull. Mus. natn. Hist. nat. Paris* 2 ser. **20** (4), 336–342.

Edgar, A. L. and Yuan, H. A. 1968. Daily locomotory activity in *Phalangium opilio* and seven species of *Leiobunum* (Arthropoda: Phalangida). *Bios.* **39** (4), 167–176.

Edgar, A. L. 1971. Studies on the biology and ecology of Michigan Phalangida (Opiliones). *Misc. Publs Mus. Zool. Univ. Mich.* **144**, 1–64.

Ekpa, O., Wheeler, J. W., Cokendolpher, J. C. and Duffield, R. M. 1985. Ketones and alcohols in the defensive secretion of *Leiobunum townsendi* Weed and a review of the known exocrine secretions of Palpatores (Arachnida: Opiliones). *Comp. Biochem. Physiol.* **81B** (3), 555–557.

Gruber, J. and Martens, J. 1968. Morphologie, Systematik und Ökologie der Gattung *Nemastoma* C. L. Koch (s. str.) (Opiliones, Nemastomatidae). *Senckenberg. biol.* **49**, 137–172.

116

Gruber, J. and Hunt, G. S. 1973. *Nelima doriae* (Canestrini) a South European harvestmen in Australia and New Zealand (Arachnida, Opiliones, Phalangiidae). *Rec. Austr. Mus.* **28** (16), 383–392.

Gruber, J. 1984. Über *Opilio canestrinii* (Thorell) und *Opilio transversalis* Roewer (Arachnida: Opiliones, Phalangiidae). *Annln naturh. Mus. Wien* **86B**, 251–273.

Gueutal, J. 1944. De l'éclosion chez un opilion: *Phalangium opilio* L. *Bull. Soc. ent. France* **49**, 24–26.

Hammen, L. van der. 1985. Comparative studies in Chelicerata III. Opilionida. *Zool. Verh. Leiden* **220**, 1–60.

Hansen, H. J. and Sørensen, W. 1904. *On two orders of Arachnida* (Opiliones and Ricinulei). 1–182. Cambridge University Press, Cambridge.

Harlow, W. M. 1924. Do Daddy-long-legs drink? *Yosemite Nature Notes* **8**, 17.

Herbst, J. F. W. 1798. Naturgeschichte der Insekten-Gattung *Opilio*. *Natursystem der Ungeflügelten Insekten*. Zweytes Heft, 1–26, Berlin.

Hillyard, P. D. 1981. *Coleosoma floridanum* Banks (Araneae, Theridiidae) and *Boeorix manducus* Thorell (Opiliones, Assamiidae): two tropical arachnids in botanical gardens. *Newsl. Br. arachnol. Soc.* **31**, 3–5.

Holmes, P. 1979. *Henderson's dictionary of biological terms*. 9th ed. 1–510. Longman, London.

Jaeger, E. C. 1955. *A source-book of biological names and terms*. 3rd ed. 1–317. Springfield, Ill.

Jennings, A. L. 1982. A new species of harvestmen of the genus *Mitopus* in Britain. *J. Zool., Lond.* **198** (1), 1–14.

Jennings, A. L. 1983. Biogeographical variation in the harvestman *Mitopus morio* (Opiliones, Arachnida). *J. Zool., Lond.* **200** (3), 367–380.

Juberthie, C. 1964. Recherches sur la biologie des opilions. *Annls Spéléol.* **19** (1), 1–238.

Kästner, A. 1928. Opiliones (Weberknechte, Kanker). In: Dahl, F. (ed.) *Die Tierwelt Deutschlands* **8** (3), 1–151.

Klee, G. E. and Butcher, J. W. 1968. Laboratory rearing of *Phalangium opilio*. *Mich. Ent.* **1** (8), 275–278.

Lawrence, R. F. 1938. The odoriferous glands of some South African harvest-spiders. *Trans. R. Soc. S. Afr.* **25** (4), 333–342.

Linnaeus, C. 1758. *Systema Naturae*. 10th ed., Vol. 1, 821 pp., Stockholm.

Lohmander, H. 1945. Arachnologische Fragmente. 2. Über die Schwedischen Arten der Opilionengattung *Oligolophus* C. L. Koch. *Göteborgs K. Vetensk.-o. vitterh Samh. Handl.* **6** (3), 15–30.

McGhee, C. R. 1977. Observations on the use of measurements in the systematic study of *Leiobunum* (Arachnida, Phalangida). *J. Arachnol.* **5**, 169–178.

Mackie, D. W. 1970. Notes on the distribution of British harvestmen. *Bull. Br. arachnol. Soc.* **1**, 84.

Manton, S. M. 1973. The evolution of arthropodan locomotory mechanisms. Part 2. Habits, morphology and evolution of the Uniramia (Onychophora, Myriapoda, Hexapoda) and comparisons with a functional review of uniramian musculature. *Zool. J. Linn. Soc.* **53** (4), 257–375.

Martens, J. 1969. Mittel-und Südeuropäische Arten der Gattung *Nelima* (Arachnida: Opiliones: Leiobunidae). *Senckenberg. biol.* **50**, 395–415.

Martens, J. 1978. Spinnentiere, Arachnida: Weberknechte, Opiliones. In: *Die Tierwelt Deutschlands* **64**, 1–464. G. Fischer Verl., Jena.

Martens, J., Hoheisel, U. and Götze, M. 1981. Comparative anatomy of the ovipositors of the Opiliones as a contribution to the phylogeny of the order (Arachnida). *Zool. Jb. Anat.* **105**, 13-76.

Martens, J. 1983. Europäische Arten der Gattung *Sabacon* Simon 1879 (Arachnida: Opiliones: Sabaconidae). *Senckenberg. biol.* **63** (3/4), 265-296.

Martens, J. 1986. Die Grossgliederung der Opiliones und die Evolution der Ordnung (Arachnida). *Actas X Congr. Int. Arachnol.* Jaca/Espana. **1**, 289-310. [Important work on genitalia].

Martens, J. 1988. Species boundary problems in Opiliones. *Newsl. Br. arachnol. Soc.* **52**, 2-4.

Martin, B. 1746. Quoted by Bristowe, 1949.

Meade, R. H. 1855. Monograph on the British species of Phalangiidae or harvestmen. *Ann. Mag. nat. Hist.* Ser. 2, **15**, 393-416.

Meade, R. H. 1861. Supplement to a monograph on the British species of Phalangiidae. *Ann. Mag. nat. Hist.* Ser. 3, **7**, 353-357.

Meijer, J. 1973. Some remarks on the systematics of the *Mitostoma chrysomelas* group (Arachnida, Opiliones, Nemastomatidae). *Zool. Meded. Leiden* **46** (9), 117-127.

Meijer, J. 1984. Different phenological strategies in two nemastomatid harvestmen (Arachnida, Opiliones, Nemastomatidae). *Bull. Br. arachnol. Soc.* **6** (5), 211-216.

Merrett, C. 1984. A further discovery of the harvestman *Sabacon* in Glamorgan. *Newsl. Br. arachnol. Soc.* **40**, 2.

Milner, A. R. 1985. News and views. *Nature* **314** (28 March), 320-321.

Morel, G. 1978. Les maladies microbiennes des Arachnides (Acariens exceptés). *Symp. zool. Soc. Lond.* **42**, 477-481.

Mouffet, T. 1634. *Insectorum sive minimorum animalium theatrum.* Theodore de Mayerne, London, 326 pp.

Muchmore, W. B. 1963. Two European arachnids new to the United States. *Ent. News* **74**, 208-210.

Pabst, W. 1953. Zur Biologie der mittleuropäischen Troguliden. *Zool. Jb. Syst.* **82**, 1-46.

Pack-Beresford, D. R. 1926. A list of the harvest-spiders of Ireland. *Proc. R. Ir. Acad.* **73B** (15), 125-140.

Parker, J. R. 1982. Whats in a name? – The harvestmen. *Newsl. Br. arachnol. Soc.* **33**, 1-2.

Petrunkevitch, A. 1949. A study of Palaeozoic Arachnida. *Trans. Conn. Acad. Sci.* **37**, 69-315.

Phillipson, J. 1959. The seasonal occurrence, life histories and fecundity of harvest-siders (Phalangida, Arachnida) in the neighbourhood of Durham City. *Entomologist's mon. Mag.* **95**, 134-138.

Phillipson, J. 1960a. A contribution to the feeding biology of *Mitopus morio* (F.) (Phalangida). *J. anim. Ecol.* **29**, 35-43.

Phillipson, J. 1960b. The food consumption of different instars of *Mitopus morio* (F.) (Phalangida) under natural conditions. *J. anim. Ecol.* **29**, 299-307.

Pickard-Cambridge, O. 1890. Monograph of the British Phalangidea or harvest-men. *Proc. Dorset nat. Hist. antiq. Fld Club* **11**, 163-216.

Pickard-Cambridge, O. 1897. British Arachnida observed and captured in 1896. *Proc. Dorset nat. Hist. antiq. Fld Club* **18**, 108-115.

Rambla, M. 1965. Sobre *Dicranopalpus caudatus* Dresco 1948. *Publnes Inst. Biol. apl. Barcelona* **38**, 97-104.

118

Rambla, M. 1986. Nuevos datos sobre *Dicranopalpus ramosus* (Simon, 1909) (Arachnida, Opiliones, Phalangiidae). *Actas X Congr. Int. Arachnol.* Jaca/ Espana 1, 373–382.

Roewer, C. F. 1912. Revision der Opiliones Palpatores (= Opiliones Plagiostethi). II. Teil: Familie der Phalagiidae (Subfamilien Sclerosomini, Oligolophinae, Phalangiini). *Abh. naturw. Ver. Hamburg* 20 (1), 1–295.

Roewer, C. F. 1914. Die Familien der Ischyropsalidae und Nemastomatidae der Opiliones Palpatores. *Arch. Naturg.* 80A, 99–169.

Roewer, C. F. 1923. *Die Weberknechte der Erde*. Systematische Bearbeitung der bisher bekannten Opiliones. 1–1116. Verl. G. Fischer. Jena.

Sankey, J. H. P. 1948. British harvest-spiders. *Essex Nat.* 38, 181–191.

Sankey, J. H. P. 1949a. On the harvestman *Opilio saxatilis* (C. L. Koch). *Proc. zool. Soc. Lond.* 109, 297–300.

Sankey, J. H. P. 1949b. Observations on food, enemies and parasites of British harvest-spiders (Arachnida, Opiliones). *Entomologist's mon. Mag.* 85, 246–247.

Sankey, J. H. P. 1951. Notes on the lateral distribution of some British harvest-spiders (Arachnida, Opiliones). *Entomologist's mon. Mag.* 87, 238–239.

Sankey, J. H. P. 1953a. *Nemastoma lugubre* Müller: first record of var. *unicolor* Roewer in Britain. *Ann. Mag. nat. Hist.* 12 (6), 27–29.

Sankey, J. H. P. 1953b. Further records of British harvest-spiders (Arachnida, Opiliones) with a note on *Nelima fuscifrons* (Simon), possibly new to Britain. *Entomologist* 86, 116–117.

Sankey, J. H. P. and Storey, M. W. 1969. *Dicranopalpus caudatus* Dresco (Arachnida, Opiliones), first records in Britain and France. *Entomologist's mon. Mag.* 105, 106–107.

Sankey, J. H. P. and Savory, T. H. 1974. British Harvestmen. *Synopses Br. Fauna* No. 4, 1–76.

Sankey, J. H. P. 1988. Provisional Atlas of the harvest-spiders (Arachnida: Opiliones) of the British Isles. Huntingdon: Biological Records Centre, 36 pp.

Savory, T. H. 1938. Notes on the biology of harvestmen. *J. Quekett microsc. Club* Ser. IV. 1 (2), 1–6.

Savory, T. H. 1977. *Arachnida*. 2nd Ed. 1–340. Academic Press, London.

Shear, W. A. 1975. The opilionid genera *Sabacon* and *Tomicomerus* in America (Opiliones, Ischyropsalidae). *J. Arachnol.* 3 (1), 5–29.

Shear, W. A. 1982. Opiliones. In: Parker, S. P. (ed.) *Synopsis and classification of living organisms*. Vol. 2, 104–110. McGraw-Hill, New York.

Šilhavý, V. 1961. Die Grundsätze der modernen Weberknechttaxonomie und Revision des bisherigen Systems der Opilioniden. *Verh. II. Internat. Kongr. Ent. Wien* 1960 1, 262–267.

Simon, E., 1879. 4ᵉ Ordre. – Opiliones Snd. In: *Les Arachnides de France* 7, 116–311.

Slagsvold, T. 1979. Environmental and morphological variation of *Mitopus morio* (Fabr.) (Opiliones) in Norway. *J. Biogeogr.* 6 (3), 267–276.

Snodgrass, R. E. 1948. The feeding organs of Arachnida including mite and ticks. *Smithson, misc. Collns* 110 (10), 1–93.

Spoek, G. L. 1963. The Opilionida (Arachnida) of the Netherlands. *Zool. Verh. Leiden* 63, 1–70.

Stipperger, H. 1928. Biologie und Verbreitung der Opilionen Nordtirols. *Arb. zool. Inst. Univ. Innsbruck* 3, 19–79.

Sunderland, K. D. and Sutton, S. L. 1980. A serological study of arthropod predation on woodlice in a dune grassland ecosystem. *J. anim. Ecol.* **49**, 987–1004.

Sundevall, J. C. 1833. *Conspectus Arachnidum.* Londini Gothorum, 39 pp.

Todd, V. 1949. The habits and ecology of the British harvestmen (Arachnida, Opiliones), with special reference to those of the Oxford district. *J. anim. Ecol.* **18** (2), 209–229.

Todd, V. 1950. The prey of harvestmen. *Entomologist's mon. Mag.* **86**, 252–254.

Wasgestian-Schaller, Ch. 1967. Die Autotomie-Mechanismen an den Laufbeinen der Weberknechte (Arachnida, Opiliones). *Diss. Naturwiss. Fak. Univ. Frankfurt.*

Welbourn, C. 1983. Potential use of trombidioid and erythraeoid mites as biological control agents of insect pests. In: *Biological control of pests by mites.* Hoy, M. A. et al (Eds.), 103–141, University of California, Berkeley, U.S.A.

Westwood, J. O. 1874. *Thesaurus Entomologicus Oxoniensis* **37**, 202.

Winkler, D. 1957. Die Entwicklung der äusseren Körpergestalt bei den Phalangiidae (Opiliones). *Mitt. zool. Mus. Berl.* **33**, 355–389.

Wood, S. P., Panchen, A. L. and Smithson, T. R. 1985. A terrestrial fauna from the Scottish Lower Carboniferous. *Nature* **314** (28 March) 355–356.

Wood, J. G. 1861–63. *The Illustrated Natural History.* 3 vols. Routledge, London.

Taxonomic index

For genera and species valid names are given in italic type and synonyms in roman type. All supergeneric categories are given in capitals.